Building Shooters

Applying Neuroscience Research to
Tactical Training System Design and Training Delivery

Dustin P. Salomon

and

Innovative Services and Solutions LLC
Silver Point, Tennessee

Praise for *Building Shooters*

"An incredibly logical and analytical look at firearms training. This book should have been written years ago, as understanding the material in it is critical to the development of anyone who wants to really learn how to shoot well. *Building Shooters* is an eye opening look at the problems and solution facing trainers and trainees in the area of firearms skill development. The breakdown of neural network types and the procedural memory system is worth the price of admission. Absolutely brilliant material."

— Mike Seeklander
   Owner, *Shooting-Performance*
   USPSA Grandmaster and Steel Challenge World Champion
   Host of *Shooting Performance TV* and *The American Warrior Show*
   Author of *The Art of Instruction: Your Complete Guide to
      Instructional Excellence*

"The first book of its kind, *Building Shooters* details how to effectively and efficiently teach the art of shooting by evaluating what is understood about the brain. This book is written as a literature review which begins to connect the dots between how we train, using what is known about the fundamentals of brain function. Dustin Salomon has distilled the teaching of defensive shooting to its core elements, as he looks at alternatives to current paradigms, explaining why they may not produce optimal results, while offering alternatives that will. Given an environment of budgetary pressure on such training programs, this book answers the call to look outside the box. He seeks to maximize consolidation of procedural and declarative memory, in the most efficient way possible, using a minimum amount of resources."

— Jeremy Sword
   Ph.D., Neuroscience

"With the goal of improving training implementation and delivery of firearm and tactical skills, Dustin Salomon presents a reasoned and science based foundation for his training system. The science of human performance is well explained and practical suggestions are made with a focus on developing better shooters who perform at higher levels and retain their skills longer. We employ many of his recommendations in our academy and improvements in our firearms program are measurable in terms of shooter success. This is essential reading for academy staff, curriculum developers and the firearms instructor."

— Art Aplan
   Advanced Training Coordinator
   Law Enforcement Training, Division of Criminal Investigation,
      South Dakota

"As a long time trainer this is my first opportunity to consider how the human brain receives, retains, and categorizes information. The importance is critical for how we design training. I note that *Building Shooters'* advocacy for using "live" weapons for role player training is innovative and has benefits. Challenging traditional notions is how we improve training delivery, content, and success on the street.

I look forward to your continuing research."

— Allen Garber
   US Army Ranger Captain and Combat Veteran
   FBI Supervisory Special Agent and SWAT Team Leader (Ret.)
   Police Chief, Champlin, Minnesota 1993-1999
   Commissioner, Minnesota Department of Natural Resources, 1999-2002
   U.S. Marshall, District of Minnesota 2002-2006

"*Building Shooters* is science applied to the training of the next generation of law enforcement. As a firearms instructor of new recruits in a college based system, I have found that recruits in general do not bring the same skill set to training as past generations. Gone are the days of veterans and the mechanically inclined. As a result, new recruits have no base knowledge of machinery let alone the mechanics of a firearm. As a firearms instructor that has delivered training in a traditional way, I have observed a large quantity of students required remedial training after a full cycle of basic firearms instruction. When a student has reached the 7th day of firearms instruction and still cannot locate a slide lock or magazine release, they have not grasped the workings of the machine called a handgun. Is it fair to the student to expect that someone who has never changed a bike tire as a child now learn to shoot, field strip, clean and clear a malfunction in a Glock 17 in one week? We as professional instructors have a responsibility to our students to give them the skills to survive. *Building Shooters* outlines a method of instruction that utilizes the way our brain processes information so they have the tools to survive."

— Brad Leach
    Captain, Burnsville, Minnesota Police Department (Ret.) and
        former SWAT Team Leader
    Former Instructor, Center for Criminal Justice and Law Enforcement,
        St. Paul, Minnesota
    Current Firearms Instructor for Retired Officers and Responsible Citizens

"Mr. Salomon's application of neuroscience, coupled with known training techniques, can be the next breakthrough in developing a training regimen that engages physical, mental, and psychological attributes to obtain a better end product."

— Jim H.
    Professional Firearms Instructor

Preface

The foundation for this body of research into instructional systems and methods for more efficient and effective firearms and tactical training delivery began in 2001. In the aftermath of the attack on the *USS Cole*, the US Navy significantly increased its focus on force-protection measures and small-arms training. During this time period, I was a young naval officer, newly assigned to a warship as the gunnery/fire control officer. I was tasked with training and qualifying approximately two hundred crew members in various weapon systems, ranging from the M9 pistol to the M2 heavy machine gun, to support implementation of the navy's new force-protection standards. Among the challenges I faced were a lack of training ammunition, a shortage of range availability, limited access to the personnel who required the training due to other work tasking, and inconsistent levels of support from other parts of the command leadership team. This lack of support ranged from tacit acceptance to open hostility toward the implementation of standards-based qualification and training that went beyond the level of a "check the box" familiarization. The resultant training program, while ultimately recognized as highly successful by the command leadership, was based not on what was desirable to me as a trainer but rather on what was possible given our significant organizational resource limitations.

I subsequently transferred to the Mobile Security Forces as the plank-owning operations officer for Mobile Security Detachment TWENTY TWO. Because of the force-protection-specific mission, I was able to justify support for the development, funding, and delivery of a more traditional weapons training program. This included multiple high-round-count shooting packages for my detachment. In comparison to the levels of skill that had developed as a result of the admittedly haphazard shipboard training program, I was both surprised and disappointed to find that the level of skill produced by a more traditional training approach was not significantly higher, particularly when balanced against the much higher expenditure of resources and time. I also discovered that in order to reach the desired performance standards, many of my students actually required a "less is more" approach specific to the amount of ammunition expended as well as an increased focus on dry-weapons-handling drills.

These experiences prompted the beginning of what is now nearly fifteen years of ongoing research into training methods for firearms and other tactical skill sets. The objective of these efforts has been to develop a wholly different approach than the standard training model, one that facilitates efficient and effective delivery of firearms and tactical training in environments that are constrained by limited funding, facilities, and resources.

Dustin P. Salomon, CPP

Owner and Founder

Innovative Services and Solutions LLC

Introduction and Acknowledgments

This book outlines a novel and highly effective approach to tactical training system design and training delivery. The approach outlined here is unique not only because it is based in applied neuroscience but also because it is not designed around the requirements of elite operators or shooters; it is designed specifically for the needs of the majority of armed professionals who do not have access to "enough" time, ammunition, special facilities, training packages, or resources. It is worth noting that while the specialized "1 percent" receives most of the resources, the remaining 99 percent still performs most of the actual gunfighting. There are many reasons for this (all of which are valid) but none of which change the ground-level truth. Most people who carry guns for a living suffer from inadequate entry-level training and inadequate in-service training. Additionally, those who are responsible for them are plagued with never-ending challenges and resource limitations that affect operational performance potential. These painful realities cannot be wished away or brushed aside. They are facts.

This research was conducted specifically to explain how and why our field-proven alternatives to the accepted training paradigm not only work but in fact work much better than the traditional model. Adhering to the principles of instruction and training design outlined in this book will facilitate the development of higher levels of skill and increased levels of survivability to armed professionals, with a decreased dependence upon special facilities, funding, and resources. These methods will improve the efficiency of training, enhance long-term performance results, and may forever change the level of what is possible in terms of realistic and sustainable operational performance capabilities for organizations whose missions require tactical skill sets.

This book outlines both a theory of learning applicable to tactical environments and a method that can be used to exploit it to produce better results with fewer resources. The baseline training methodology is field proven; the learning theory behind it is science.

As this work is heavily based in scientific research, it is worth noting that, by definition, science is a question, not an answer. Therefore, we view this book and the research, science, and methods contained in it as a beginning rather than as an end. This research has resulted in at least as many new questions as it has provided answers thus far and has opened what we believe are several new and exciting possibilities for both future scientific study and continued training method development. We hope and intend for our research to continue and for continuous improvement to increasingly become a hallmark of the tactical training industry.

While the full list of acknowledgments for those who have assisted would be prohibitively long, we would like to thank Dr. Catherine Harrison and Dr. Jeremy Sword for their input, direction, and advice regarding the neuroscience. Any errors in the discussion of the science are ours. Also, many thanks to Larry Yatch of Sealed Mindset; Mike Seeklander of Shooting Performance; Brian Vickers of Victory Tactical; Art Aplan; Oz E.; Brad Leach; Dustin Reynolds; Jon M.; Patrick C.; Rick S.; and Janet S. for their review, critiques, and input regarding their specific areas of expertise. Thank you also to the Navy Combat Pistol Alumni and the many fine coaches and mentors who worked with us including Junior O.; Tim M.; Kirk H.; Glen M.; Rich B.; and Brian D. Many thanks also go to our students who have provided critical feedback for improvement over the years and, above all, to those who still have the watch…thank you.

Contents and Method

We provide an overview of the principles, concepts, and scientific research behind our Integrated Skill Development and Integrated Skill Enhancement concepts. We begin by discussing the challenges faced by the training industry and then establishing a framework for discussion through outlining the performance of the human brain, not as a biological entity but as an information system.

An instructor's objective is to place information into the student's brain in such a way that it is recalled effectively when it is needed. Therefore it is important for instructors to understand how the brain's information system works and how it both stores and retrieves information in response to differing instructional techniques, environmental conditions, and stimuli.

After establishing this framework, we conduct an analysis of the operational needs that define this genre of training. This includes the specific types of skills involved and how the information that embodies these skill areas is encoded, stored, transferred, and retrieved by the brain's information system. We then examine a series of objectives and priorities that guide determining what information and information storage locations are important for our purposes. This includes description and explanation of the different factors that affect how critical information is stored in the brain as well as what part of the brain the information should be placed in to facilitate optimal storage and retrieval under operational conditions.

We then propose a modeling tool designed to facilitate training system design from a neurological basis. Using the tool, information may be targeted to specific brain areas by design, and the inherent limitations of the human brain may be considered during the process of training development.

We subsequently apply the modeling tool to conduct an overview of the existing training model. This includes an analysis considering neural-network formation within the brain's information system and the ultimate effects this has on skill development, retention, retrieval, and operational performance.

Next we propose a new model of training, applicable to both initial training (integrated skill development) and to ongoing sustainment and proficiency training applications (integrated skill enhancement). We then analyze this model while considering neural-network formation and its effects on skill development, retention, retrieval, and operational performance.

Finally, we discuss practical applications of this training system design technology to improve training design and delivery in the field. We also discuss several of the future opportunities for research that our work to date has highlighted.

Chapter 1

Defining the Problem[1]

By any standard, providing firearms and tactical training to armed professionals is a challenging profession that isn't getting any easier. Even just at the surface level, the subject matter is deadly serious, and the tools involved are dangerous. Serious injury or death is an omnipresent possibility, even during the most benign training evolutions.

Sadly, acknowledgment of the risks involved is where most people's analysis stops. This is unfortunate because physical risk doesn't even begin to scratch the surface in terms of defining the challenges that every trainer, training department, and administrator with training oversight responsibilities faces every single day. With this in mind, let us briefly examine these challenges, the forces of influence that shape our industry, and how recent advances in neuroscience can help us find solutions for the future.

Challenges Facing the Training Industry

Educational

First, risk aside, the purely educational challenge of firearms and tactical training is a daunting task. To put it in perspective, our formal educational system spends billions annually attempting to teach young Americans how to recognize and pronounce the never-changing sounds made by our twenty-six-symbol, phonetic language with enough proficiency to communicate effectively.

---

[1] The information in this was originally part of a longer piece entitled, "Throwing Away the Box: How Neuroscience Will Help Reinvent the Tactical Training Paradigm." It was originally published in Michael Seeklander's book, The Art of Instruction (Shooting Performance 2014).

In its efforts to accomplish this (among other tasks), the education system has at its disposal twelve consecutive years of schooling with access to students for nine months per year, seven hours per day, five days per week. And it routinely fails.

In contrast, the job of a tactical firearms trainer is to prepare a student to *maybe* perform an unknown skill or series of skills (that most of them never want to actually perform) under unknown conditions at some unknown future date and time. We say unknown because a deadly force encounter could involve close-contact shooting, one-handed shooting, two-handed shooting, ground fighting, shooting on the move, engaging a moving threat, engaging multiple threats, firing multiple rounds, support-handed shooting, close-quarters surgical shooting, positional shooting, distance shooting, shooting from cover, low-light shooting, malfunction clearance, and so on…or some combination thereof.

The first thing that can be stated with certainty is that optimally successful skill performance will involve some combination of fine (trigger manipulation/visual focus on the front sight blade) and gross (limb movement/ mobility) motor skills.

The unknown skill or series of skills (should performance ever become necessary) will also be performed (at said unknown time) in response to an unknown stimulus or series of stimuli, the interpretation of which may heavily depend upon an unknown context. In order to achieve successful skill performance, these (unknown) stimuli and context(s) must be cognitively evaluated and interpreted against a complex system of parameters (law and policy). If this cognitive processing is performed erroneously (even if the skill itself is performed and applied correctly), tragic loss of life, serious injury, damage to property, and felony criminal conviction are all potential results. In any case, the results of real-world skill performance for the student will always involve consequences regarding loss of life, serious injury, criminal liability, civil liability, and loss of livelihood.

As if this situation were not already challenging enough, biology has added an additional wrinkle. Scientists call it the sympathetic nervous system. Commonly known as "fight or flight," the sympathetic nervous system takes control of human performance during highly stressful situations, such as life and death encounters. This consists largely of the effects from a rapid natural-chemical injection (adrenaline) designed to provide the capacity for otherwise superhuman strength and endurance. Unfortunately, the sympathetic nervous system also has its drawbacks, particularly for gunfighting and most especially for gunfighting under strict policy parameters and legal oversight.

For example, the chemicals' presence in the brain tissue serves to interfere with normal cognitive processes. This makes complex decision-making, information recall, and data analysis next to impossible. It also affects vision and hearing, sometimes causing what are commonly known as audio and visual exclusion—hearing becomes virtually impossible, and field of vision becomes a literal tunnel or even disappears entirely. The increased physical strength, endurance, and pain resistance associated with adrenaline also come at a price, as fine motor skills (needed for delicately manipulating a trigger, moving a small safety lever, closing one eye, or shifting visual focus to achieve clarity on a small front sight post) become all but impossible to perform.

In fact, the second (and final) thing that can be said with certainty about the potential skill performance we are training our students for is that if that moment ever comes, their bodies will physiologically lose their normal capacity to perform most of the functions required for both successful skill(s) performance and a successful operational outcome.

And, as if this all weren't quite enough of a challenge, most law enforcement trainers must also accomplish all of this (for more than one weapon system) in approximately two weeks. This is followed by an average of about eight additional hours every six months for in-service training, which brings us to the next challenge facing our industry: Resources.

Resources

As noted above, training time is always at a premium. Some of this is due to budgetary limitations, some of this is due to policy, some of this is due to facility availability, some of this is due to a lack of student interest, and some is due to increasing demands on training departments. These demands take the form of ever-expanding operational requirements (new gizmos require new training) and ever-increasing expectations of field performance (video cameras on Internet-connected smartphones have, in many ways, changed the game).

Unfortunately, finding and scheduling productive time between students, trainers, and facilities is not the only resourced-based challenge. A new era of postsequester austerity has crimped many organizations' overall access to resources, which has somewhat affected their ability to conduct firearms and tactical training. Additionally, shortages of ammunition that seem to occur incrementally, based largely around domestic political cycles, have certainly presented a challenge, not to mention the increased cost of current ammunition.

For many trainers, facility availability (range and other) is also a huge challenge. In some locales, firing ranges are considered by public officials to be something akin to a particularly loathsome cross between toxic waste dumps and ceremonial grounds for satanic rituals. Even in politically range-friendly areas, noise and environmental ordinances can still make range operation extremely challenging. There also always seem to be one or two "neighbors" who are insistent upon shutting down any active range in their community for one reason or another. In areas where range facilities are present, convenient, and stable, they are often expensive to rent and usually even more expensive to own, maintain, and operate.

Even where and when adequate range facilities are available, cost-effective, and convenient, they often do not facilitate safe or effective training in some of the areas required to both match operational requirements and mitigate the significant (and increasing) liability that faces tactical firearms users, particularly law enforcement. Examples of these areas include moving targets, multiple targets (moving and static), decision shooting, employing multiple levels of force, low light, team tactical applications, and multidirectional engagements. Simulator technology such as Simunition, UTM, FATS, PRISM, and so on can provide some assistance to trainers in many of these areas; however, these can sometimes be prohibitively expensive—even more so than live fire—and all carry their own limitations and level of associated risk.

Students

Sadly, a near-impossible task combined with significant resource limitations aren't all that define the challenges facing our industry. We also face significant obstacles relating to our students. Some, particularly upon initial training, are irrationally afraid of both the subject matter and the tools themselves. Others have previous (and incorrect) experience that hampers their performance potential. For some applications, the students may not even speak the same language as their instructors. Still others, particularly in the professional realm of security, military, and law enforcement, aren't actually all that interested in learning what we need to teach them. In fact, some of them are downright hostile to the experience, especially during in-service training and periodic qualification.

These "hostile" individuals often skate by, meeting the bare minimum administratively driven standards of performance that facilitate their continued employment. Unfortunately, these standards are often designed more to justify placing an officer into an active billet to fulfill manning requirements than they are to measure the officer's potential to perform during a critical incident. Yet, since these officers *do* meet the minimum required standards, there is seemingly nothing that can be done to gain their attention or effort during training, despite the benefits this effort would bring to them, their teammates, the organization as a whole, and the general public.

Administrative Support

Certainly no discussion of the challenges facing tactical trainers, particularly those in the realms of professional security, military, and law enforcement, would be complete without discussing the much-criticized (albeit sometimes unfairly) "management." Administrators have very different jobs than operational personnel or trainers do, and therefore they tend to view the world through a somewhat different lens than those on the street or those in the training department.

Administrators and managers are responsible for much more than simply ensuring that officers have the tactical training and qualifications necessary to perform the job. In their world, budget constraints, other training requirements, organizational liability, morale, public relations, and long-term manning issues are every bit as important as tactical and firearms training. At times, trainers tend to scoff at these other issues in frustration, especially when they are presented as conflicting priorities with training programs. However, this does not change the reality that these other priorities *are* important and can often affect the day-to-day operations of organizations just as significantly (albeit usually with somewhat reduced personal severity) as priorities within the firearms and tactical realm.

Challenges Summary

The bottom line is that providing effective firearms and tactical training, particularly to armed professionals, is a very difficult line of work. Trainers face a myriad of unique challenges, particularly with respect to educational objectives. Also, the reality is that, due to finite time and finite resource availability, training programs will *always* conflict with other organizational priorities. Therefore, it is incumbent upon us as trainers to continually develop, update, and enhance our methods to improve both the effectiveness of what we do in terms of its impact on operational proficiency and the efficiency of how we do it.

Forces That Influence the Training Industry

As we seek to improve our programs, it is instructive to take a step back and look at the influencing forces that shape our industry as a whole. Presently, there are four: vendors, competitive shooting, elite units, and liability. The first three of these forces are internal to the industry. They are tremendously supportive, both of our industry and of each other; each brings a series of unique benefits that makes it invaluable and irreplaceable. However, each of these first three has a set of tremendous differences when compared to the needs of the vast majority of armed professionals and those who train them. And all four of these influences bring their own set of inherent liabilities and limitations that ultimately impact our ability to design and implement efficient and effective training.

19

Vendors

Vendors are a tremendously important sector of influence within of our industry. They provide equipment and training as well as help drive innovation within the industry, especially as it relates to equipment and facility capability. However, both vendors and the innovation they provide have their limitations.

First and foremost, vendors exist to make a profit. This isn't a bad thing; it is simply a statement of fact. Without turning a profit, vendors cease to exist, and the whole industry loses as a result. Because of this profit requirement, most sales teams can be counted upon to attempt to close on every possible sale, rattling off the various features and benefits of their products and demonstrating why one or another is the best fit for virtually any given situation or requirement, whether it truly is or not.

As businesses, vendors are incentivized to accomplish two things. The first is to create a new "need" within the market space. In other words, one of their objectives is to develop a proprietary piece of technology or equipment that the industry cannot live without. The second is to create a literal dependency on their products, convincing their customers that they could not continue to function effectively without the vendor and its support. Again, there is nothing wrong with this. It is the essence of free-market economics. On the other hand, from our perspective as trainers, each "need" that is developed has the potential to become both a limitation and a liability in our capacity to develop and deliver efficient and effective training.

For example, if Acme Tactical Supply Company develops a new widget that becomes indispensable in training, even becoming a part of the written training policy and industry-accepted standards for training delivery, then this is great news for Acme Tactical Supply. It's also very likely a boon to the industry in general, since this particular widget probably provides an important capability and is a great aid/tool for trainers. However, no matter how great the capability of the widget, *dependency* on it to provide training creates a limitation. What if said widget is expensive, and one is required for each individual during training? What if an organization can only afford four widgets—or if sixteen of the twenty widgets were accidentally left in the vehicle that was turned into the motor pool last night for maintenance? In these cases, dependence on the widget means that only four people in the organization could train at once. This would significantly strain already limited time and manpower resources and therefore could ultimately reduce, rather than enhance, the organization's training capability.

In short, while vendors and their products are tremendous and irreplaceable assets to the industry, overdependence on them for delivering effective training is often both inefficient and indicative of artificially imposed limitations on potential training effectiveness.

Competitors

Competitors are another wonderful and tremendously influential segment of the industry, the professional athletes of shooting. They are often also heavily involved in the industry as training vendors. Professional competitors have the opportunity to travel extensively, talk to thousands of people per year, influence vendors' designs and development of equipment, and help cross-pollinate ideas from one segment of the industry to another. They are also the true technical experts when it comes to fundamental skill performance and are continuously pushing the envelope in terms of what is possible to achieve with the limits of human and equipment performance.

Nevertheless, despite all the benefits that the competitive side of the industry provides, it also has its limitations in terms of its focus, skills, equipment, and expectations of performance. Competitive practical shooting is focused on blending a balance of speed and accuracy to achieve a winning score. There is nothing wrong with this; however, it simply is not the same focus that people who carry a gun for gunfighting should have. True, real-world application of tactical firearms skills demands not only a level of fundamental skill but also the ability to analyze data, respond to stimuli, and make decisions—preferably decisions that prevent the application of deadly force from ever becoming necessary, especially for most law enforcement mission requirements. Optimal performance on the street demands fine-tuning very different skills than those that are necessary for optimal performance in competition.

For example, successful competitors win matches largely because they have honed their stage tactics, split times, reload times, and target transitions to a fine edge and have balanced these skills with enough accuracy to achieve winning scores. In a gunfight, however, none of these specific skills tend to matter much, as long as a baseline ability to perform at an acceptable professional level exists. Consider that in handgun competition, consistent split times of 0.28 seconds at 7 yards and 2-second reloads will assure that a shooter can never achieve significant success. Operationally, however, these same levels of skill performance are more than sufficient for any application.

Furthermore, the single most decisive factor in the majority of real-world situations (assuming that an acceptable baseline of fundamental skill) is human-stimulus-based decision-making. Assuming that both shooters have a reasonable level of accuracy, a shooter who consistently draws in 1.8 seconds and has 0.3-second splits will always lose in competition to a shooter who consistently draws in 1.2 seconds and has 0.18-second splits. In fact, it won't even be close. However, in the real world, whichever of these shooters makes the quickest and best decisions is probably going to prevail; the fractions of a second are virtually irrelevant.

This point should not in any way be interpreted as discouragement against the development of high levels of fundamental skill. It is simply a cautionary note against the self-imposition of unnecessary limitations within training programs due to modeling performance expectations against competitive shooting standards. If standards and training are designed around the basis of the expectations for successful competitive performance, then it is likely that an inordinate amount of the limited training time will be focused in this direction. This may result in the exclusion of other skills, even if those other skills may ultimately be much more important for operational success.

When very tight tolerances in terms of standards of performance become mandatory job requirements, there is also the danger that students will adjust their range equipment to optimize success during training and qualification, even if this equipment configuration is not operationally viable. When this occurs, not only is a tremendous amount of potential training benefit lost, but training scars may also be developed. Personnel may even operationally utilize completely unproven equipment that they have never used in training.

In summary, competition shooting is a highly valuable resource and a tremendously positive influence on our industry. However, the specific skills that result in competitive success, competitive standards, and competitive equipment may all be very different from those that will optimize chances for operational success. These differences, in some cases, may be harmful operationally and can also lead to the unintentional imposition of limitations that may hamper the development of a training structure that produces optimal real-world results.

Elite Units

The other highly significant internal influencing force on our industry is the collection of elite units from the world's militaries and law enforcement organizations such as Delta Force, Seal Team Six, LAPD SWAT, the FBI's Hostage Rescue Team (HRT), and so on. Overall, these units (and others) contribute a tremendous amount to the industry as a whole. They test and develop equipment. They also design, validate, and operationally vet tactics, the results of which eventually filter down to other military units as well as law enforcement and private security. All of this is beneficial. There is little doubt that these units represent some of the best of the best in terms of their personnel. There is also no doubt that their capabilities are operationally validated and that their personnel are a wealth of knowledge and experience in tactics, techniques, procedures, training, and equipment.

However, there are some significant and fundamental differences between elite units' structures, their operations, the methods that they use to train, and the structure, operations, and training of the vast majority of armed professionals. Because of their reputations and operational credentials, many in the industry attempt to replicate them, particularly in their training methodology. Unfortunately, sometimes this is done in such a way that the training actually limits, rather than enhances, an organization's performance.

These specialized units have very specific mission areas, which sometimes require unique and specialized tactics and equipment. Tactics in particular are highly misunderstood across the industry, as individuals tend to become wrapped up in this technique or that technique and the inherent superiority of one over the other. This leads to the common quip that tactics are much like the south end of a northbound donkey: every jackass has one, and they all stink.

In truth, while some techniques can be generally superior, it is very important to take a step back from the emotion of the debate and recognize, at a fundamental level, what tactics actually are. Specifically, they are utilizing techniques and procedures that apply your own capabilities and strengths against your enemy's limitations and weaknesses based on the environment and the terrain, while minimizing the enemy's potential to reverse the process.

In other words, the "right" tactic depends heavily upon your own abilities and limitations, the abilities and limitations of your adversary, the environment and conditions you are working in, and the terrain that you are on. This effectively means that the techniques, equipment, and procedures for both operations and for training that work extremely well for a group of highly trained commandos operating in South East Asia could prove to be nothing short of a disaster if applied by a part-time, suburban SWAT team in the United States—and vice versa.

Elite units are also very different in terms of their personnel requirements and selection criteria. They have the luxury of utilizing their entry-level training programs as a highly discriminatory selection process, sometimes dismissing 75 percent or more of their candidates annually. They have a virtually unlimited supply of highly motivated applicants, and instructors are often empowered to fail every single student if they feel it is necessary. Even after becoming a member of these units, operators can be subject to random performance testing, and failure may result in immediate dismissal from the unit.

Contrast this with the typical law enforcement, military or private security endeavor where, in many cases, manning requirements can dictate that failure of students (particularly during in-service training and qualification) is almost a non-option. Or, if a student does fail, his or her employment status may continue unabated (albeit perhaps in a different capacity until he or she passes—for which the instructor may now be responsible).

Furthermore, many elite units only accept experienced applicants from other military or law enforcement organizations, meaning that all of their applicants are already trained and qualified at an operational level. This allows the instructors to use their weapons training program as a tool to eliminate all but the few candidates who are already highly proficient. Once again, contrast this with an entry-level program in the military, law enforcement, or private security where the trainer's job is not to weed out all but those few who already have the skills for the job but rather to train new personnel from the ground up for operational success.

Elite units also have access to tremendous amounts of resources, so as to be virtually unlimited in some cases. Consider that individual members of some of these units may shoot more training rounds in a single week than some entire police departments shoot in a year. Clearly, training methods that work extremely well when students have twenty-plus hours of individual range time per week and an unlimited supply of ammunition will not be successful for an organization that can only supply a few hours of range access and one box of fifty rounds twice per year. Furthermore, attempting to replicate these training methods, or even specific advanced drills pulled from these types of programs, is likely to be counterproductive if the students are not already at the performance level necessary to benefit from the drills.

In short, the equipment, tactics, and training methods utilized by elite units may not be appropriate or effective for the vast majority of armed professionals. Some may be extremely dangerous and even counterproductive, ultimately limiting the organization's overall performance potential. This doesn't mean that the tremendous experience and knowledge that comes from these units should be discounted or that their lessons learned should be ignored. It does mean that the training, tactics, techniques, and procedures should be designed for each specific organization based on its own mission, environment, capabilities, limitations, and potential adversaries.

As a point of interest, it is worth noting that the single most important attribute that contributes to the success of these types of units is *not* advanced techniques, cool equipment, or high-speed tactics. It is mastery, both individually and as a unit, of the fundamentals, from marksmanship to mission planning.

Liability

The final influencing force acting on our industry is liability. Unlike the others, it is largely an external force, yet it still plays an enormous role in shaping the industry. The first piece is operational liability; coupled with associated case law, this often drives training requirements (and not just in firearms and tactical training). While this generally provides a positive influence in terms of justifying additional training resources and forcing changes for the better in training programs, it can also create limitations when coupled with a dearth of resources.

For example, suppose that an organization has a policy of quarterly firearms training. If live-fire, low-light training were suddenly mandated once per year as a result of liability concerns but additional training hours were not allocated to meet this new requirement, then some other part of the existing training program would necessarily suffer as a result. This can ultimately result in "check the box" training, which meets paperwork requirements but, due to an insufficient allocation of resources, does little to provide actual benefit in terms of operational performance. In some cases it may even reduce it. As a result, the additional training driven by operational liability, while conceptually good, can sometimes actually limit the organization's overall performance potential.

The second piece of liability is associated with the actual training itself. This is (and should be) an omnipresent consideration during all training design and delivery. What we do is dangerous, and it takes only one small mistake for a life to be lost, which is always unacceptable in training. Even if lives aren't lost, injuries (even small ones unrelated to gunshot wounds) can result in lost time, lawsuits, insurance claims, and so on. While it is impossible to train effectively for combat while maintaining zero injuries (though zero gunshot wounds should be accepted as an axiom), training that is as likely to remove a student from the manning roster as it is to prepare them to succeed operationally is not effective, efficient, or well managed. Furthermore, consistent injuries in training will almost certainly result in a well-justified administrative "crackdown." This, in turn, may severely limit what types of training can be performed in the future, again limiting the organization's long-term capabilities.

Liability is an unavoidable, highly influential force on our industry. If it is not anticipated and managed appropriately, it can severely limit an organization's potential in both training and operational performance.

Summary of the Forces That Influence the Training Industry

The four primary influencing forces that drive the training industry—vendors, competition shooters, elite units, and liability—all provide benefits, new ideas, new directions, and new capabilities. They also have one other thing in common: they define the industry with their own limitations. These limitations range from a perceived inability to perform effective training without access to a specific piece of vendor-supplied technology to a real inability to develop student proficiency in critical fundamentals due to a liability-driven increase in the required number of training topics sans an associated increase in time and resources.

These forces can, in many ways, be thought of as a "box" that contains the current training paradigm. They provide structure and support to help address the many challenges. At the same time, they also define the limitations that govern operational performance potential across the industry.

Neuroscience and the Training Paradigm of the Future

Despite the tremendous advancements that have been made in the industry over the past few decades, today's training paradigm is, in many respects, trapped. It is confined by the limitations inherent to the forces that shape and define it. The future, which will doubtless be an era defined by growing challenges combined with diminishing resources, requires innovation and new approaches to training development and delivery that are quite literally "outside the box."Fortunately, necessity is the mother of invention. A growing body of instructors is now looking outside of the modern training paradigm's limitations and beginning to explore a new horizon for the future. This future is not one defined by limitations; it is defined by capabilities.

Human performance and behavioral neuroscience is an exciting, rapidly evolving field of scientific study that has seen tremendous advancements just within the past few years. Recent developments of new technology and new research techniques now enable scientists to study the human brain in ways that have never before been possible. These new frontiers of science can help us reach new frontiers in firearms and tactical training. By truly understanding how the human brain stores, processes, and utilizes information, we can

29

structure our training programs not around challenges and limitations but rather around operational objectives and the learning capabilities that are inherent in our students.

Chapter 2

The Brain as an Information System

The human brain is a miraculous and incredibly complex system. Even the most advanced levels of modern science are only beginning to scratch the surface in terms of understanding how the brain functions. However, the more science discovers about the human brain, the more it appears to function as a biological network of chemically enhanced electrical connections (Wolfe 2010). In many ways, the brain is very similar to a computer network, and in fact, cutting-edge computer information-system design is largely based upon modeling the function of the human brain (Murre; Jin and Sendhoff 2006).

Function and Structure

Here, we will mostly avoid specifics of the brain's anatomical, chemical, and biological structures and processes. For our purposes, we are interested in the brain purely as an information system. Like any other information system, the brain has the capability to perform a number of data-related functions. These include collection, processing (examples include filtering, organization, categorization, and pattern recognition), storage, deletion, and retrieval.

Connectionist Learning Theory

To understand how the mind works (and why understanding this is important) it is first helpful to understand the concept of connectionist learning. This is the most widely accepted theory of how data is processed and stored inside the brain (French and Ferrara 1999; Wolfe 2010). The brain's functionality results from a series of biologically generated electrical connections. Any bodily process, piece of information, physical action, sound, sight, thought, decision, or any other function that requires use of the brain is accomplished through electrical impulses that are sent from one brain cell to another. Brain cells (neurons) are in fact designed to both send and receive electrical signals (Jensen 2008; Wolfe 2010).

When electrical signals are sent from one neuron to another, a residual pathway between these two neurons remains (Wolfe 2010). When electrical signals are repeatedly sent between the same two neurons, the residual pathway between these neurons becomes increasingly defined. The connectivity of the electrical connection between the neurons also becomes stronger. This improvement in connectivity is the result of actual chemical and biological changes that occur within and between the two brain cells involved. With enough improvement, an actual "shortcut" between the neurons forms; this is the method through which the brain learns. These connections between neurons are sometimes called neural-networks, or memory traces. This phenomenon is often referred to as Hebb's Law, succinctly stated as, "The neurons that fire together wire together" (Jensen 2008).

Input

One of the primary functions of the brain is information collection. Virtually all of the information that the brain receives comes in the form of sensory input. In layman's terms, this means that electrical signals are sent from some part of the body with sensory ability (eyes, ears, nervous system, nose, etc.) into the brain's sensory receptors. These receptors constantly receive a tremendous barrage of sensory input—so much in fact that it would be overwhelming, to the point of impossibility, to consciously process it all.

To avoid the biological equivalent of a system overload, the brain utilizes a data filter. This filter sorts through the information collected by the body's various sensor systems and immediately discards most of it. Once data has advanced past this filter, it enters into the brain's information-processing and storage systems. One of the unique functions of the human brain (and one that is now being replicated in computer-information network design) is its utilization of multiple information storage and processing systems. In other words, the same information is processed and stored in multiple redundant, yet functionally separate, systems.

Short-Term Memory

The first of these systems is called the short-term memory system. Short-term memory allows the brain to process and store information for short periods of time that can range from a few seconds to days or weeks (Jensen 2008). This system includes what is commonly called working memory (Wolfe 2010). Working memory is comparable in function to a computer's RAM (random access memory) system. It facilitates the rapid and efficient availability, processing, and utilization of data associated with actively occurring actions or events.

One of the most unique and important features of the short-term memory system in general, and of working memory in particular, is that it has a limited amount of storage capacity. Similar to a computer's hard drive, there is only so much information that can be contained in it at any given time. This means that the neurons within the brain that comprise short-term memory are only capable of making a limited number of connections containing a limited amount of information. Once this limit has been reached, the short-term memory system has only one option if it receives additional data: it must replace some of the already existing information (French and Ferrara 1999). Once its storage limits have been reached, the short-term memory system is no longer sufficient for normal human function, much less for learning.

Long-Term Memory

The brain also contains multiple long-term memory systems, which allow it to compensate for the limitations of short-term memory while still capitalizing on short-term memory's unique capabilities. The short-term memory system in general and working (immediate use) memory in particular are very limited in terms of the volume of information that they can hold at any given time.

To address this problem, the brain is equipped two distinct, long-term memory systems, both of which have an enormous amount of storage capacity (Jensen 2008). These redundant yet separately functional systems help the brain compensate for the limitations of short-term memory while still capitalizing on short-term memory's unique capabilities.

These two long-term storage systems are physically located in different geographical areas of the brain (different from each other and different from short-term memory) and utilize different types of neurons and processes for the storage of information (Colon-Cesario et al. 2006). Together, they allow the brain to transfer important information out of short-term memory, thereby not only retaining the information but also freeing up short-term space to facilitate the input, processing, and storage of new data (Dennis and Wiles; McClelland et al. 1994; Kassardjian et al. 2005). The process of transferring information into long-term memory is sometimes referred to as *consolidation*.

These two distinct locations for long-term memory storage are commonly distinguished as the procedural and declarative memory systems.

These are defined by how and under what conditions the information stored in these separate partitions of long-term memory is retrieved (Wolfe 2010).

Declarative Memory

The declarative memory system is characterized by conscious recall. The information, skills, actions, and associations stored within the parameters of declarative memory require intentional effort to access. Examples of declarative memory include facts, figures, and procedures that are learned, yet require thought and effortful, conscious recall (Wolfe 2010; Shumway-Cooke and Woollacott 2012).

Procedural Memory

The procedural memory system is characterized by access without conscious effort. Examples include well-rehearsed physical actions, sequences, or responses to stimuli that happen automatically and sometimes even despite conscious intentions to the contrary (Jensen 2008; Wolfe 2010; Shumway-Cooke and Woollacott 2012).

Summary of the Brain's Function and Structure as an Information System

Information flows into the brain through acquisition by one (or more) of the body's sensory receptors. Once this information reaches the brain, it immediately goes through an automatic, unconscious filtering process. Most of the information is discarded.

After information has passed through the filter, it enters the short-term memory system. The short-term memory system keeps information readily accessible and easy to work with; however, in order to carry out these functions with a constant inflow of new information, short-term memory is very limited in its capacity to store data. Once the short-term memory system is filled to capacity, it cannot receive new information without replacing information that is already in place.

The brain is equipped with multiple, long-term information storage systems. These systems compensate for the short-term memory limitations. They allow the brain to quickly access and process information currently in use while also retaining information over long periods of time and storing quantities of information that exceed the capacity of short-term storage. Long-term storage systems are classified respectively as declarative memory and procedural memory. Declarative memory stores information that is accessed consciously. Procedural memory stores information that is accessed unconsciously, without the requirement for intentional retrieval.

Once information enters into the short-term memory system, it can be used, processed, and accessed under normal conditions. However, in order to be retained beyond the immediate period of its use and application, this information must be transferred into one of the long-term storage systems. If this transfer does not occur, the information will be displaced, discarded, or overwritten and therefore lost once new data is received.

Information Retrieval and the Stress Response

For any practical use of knowledge or skill to occur, the information stored within the brain, whether in long-term or short-term memory, must be retrieved before it can be processed or utilized. Therefore, to develop effective training, it is not sufficient to understand how information is stored; it is also important to understand how information is retrieved.

As previously discussed, firearms and tactics instruction, among all other disciplines of training, presents a unique set of challenges for instructors.

One is the fact that the distance between the date and time of training and the date and time when the information and skills will be needed operationally is always unknown. This temporal uncertainty makes it difficult to construct viable performance metrics and standards that accurately assess the training's operational effectiveness.

A second challenge is that if the training ever needs to be utilized operationally, performance will occur under the physiological conditions of the stress response and the sympathetic nervous system. These considerations, from a neurological and biological perspective, equate to a significant and sudden change in the chemistry of both the brain and the body, which has a tremendous impact on their function and capability. Specifically, high levels of stress can often mean effects such as decreased cognitive ability; altered spatial awareness, temporal perception, and sensory perception; appendage tremors; and decreased motor-skill performance (Grossman and Siddle 2000; Rash et al.).

Every capability of the mind and body that is involved in firearms manipulation and related tactical performance is impacted by significant physiological effects during all real-world operational application. Training students to overcome these difficulties presents a distinctive challenge for a multitude of reasons. For example, due to the life-or-death nature of the skills, tools, and subject matter involved, accurate replication of these operational conditions and the stress response they invoke is difficult to achieve in a training environment, particularly one governed by significant resource constraints. An equally if not even more daunting obstacle is the fact that training environments that are designed to produce similarly high fear-based stress levels tend to biologically preclude, rather than enhance, many aspects of the learning process (Duncko et al. 2009; Krugers et al. 2011; Thomas and LaBar 2008).

The objective for firearms and tactics instructors therefore becomes to structure training so as to develop the appropriate neural-networks that correspond to skill performance. These networks must be retained over long periods of time and be accessible operationally during the stress response. Traditional methods of learning, as defined by most educationally based research, are ineffective and insufficient for these requirements. Therefore, much of the traditional research and methodology for applied adult learning may not be optimal or applicable for the development of operationally focused tactical skill sets.

Chapter 3

Information/Neural-Network Types Associated with Firearms and Tactical Training

We have presented our theory that the neurological goal of tactical training system design is to develop the applicable neural-networks for knowledge, skill performance, stimulus recognition, and stimulus response. Students should both retain information over long periods of time and also naturally access the information under the effects of the stress response. To facilitate better discussion of the processes necessary to accomplish this, we will first define the different types of information and therefore the different types of neural-networks associated with the operational application of tactical skill sets.

Physical Motor Skills

Physical motor skills are the most commonly thought of and evaluated skills involved in firearms and tactical training. These skills include actions (or sequences of actions) involved with firearms manipulation such as presentation of the firearm, clearing malfunctions, gripping/holding the firearm, and pressing the trigger. For the purposes of this book, this category includes visuomotor skills that involve a combination of visual input, spatial awareness, and motor skill performance. Firearms-related examples include sight picture, sight alignment, dynamic engagements, some aspects of weapon presentation, and follow-through.

Stimulus Response and Stimulus-Initiated Skill Performance

In tactical applications, skills and procedures are often performed in response to external events or stimuli. There are a number of specific skills related purely to firearms manipulation and the technical aspect of shooting performance that also fall into this category. These include recoil management, emergency reloading, and initiation for the clearance of malfunctions. In addition, practical firearms application for police, military, or self-defense applications always involves stimulus-based skill performance. In fact, a stimulus of some sort is always required for the employment of a weapon or performance of a skill in an operational environment.

Associative/Environmental Skill Performance (Contextual)

Not only are specific stimuli important for firearms use and tactical application, but environmental and contextual considerations are critical as well. For example, on a shooting range, the sound of a buzzer may be a specific stimulus associated with drawing and firing a weapon. Inside a convenience store, this same stimulus response would be tragically inappropriate. Not only is contextual association with skill performance and decision-making important operationally, but also there is significant scientific evidence that properly applied contextual training can be useful for enhancing learning, controlling stimulus response, and improving performance (Berthouze and Tijsseling 2006; McIntyre and Roozendaal 2007; Wiskott et al. 2004).

Associative Judgment and Decision-Making

One of the most significant challenges in the operational application of tactical skills in the real world is the judgment and decision-making associated with the application of deadly force. Most training models treat this as an instantaneous decision based on a specific set of environmental conditions and stimuli. While snap use-of-force decisions do occur in the field, most lethal encounters are more accurately described as the result of a progressive series of associative decisions, judgments, and actions based on stimuli.

It is also worth noting that a great deal of firearms-related skill application in the real world does *not* involve the use of lethal force. Examples include use of the weapon as a deterrent and decisions about muzzle position, weapons condition, carriage method, and posture. Ultimately, the judgment and decision-making associated with the application of firearms and tactical skills in the field involve developing expanded neural-networks that link the memory traces for physical skills, stimulus response, and contextual/environmental association with those of the applicable cognitive processes.

Skill and Contextual Modification and Transfer

Not only must skills and stimulus response be applied based upon context and judgment, but successful operational applications can often involve the modification of skills, sequences, and processes (including innovation and invention) for adaptation to new environments or to accomplish novel objectives. Modification of learned skills and the ability to adapt skills, associations, and judgments to new contexts and stimuli without prior training is sometimes referred to as *learning transfer*. Far from being an innate ability, effective learning transfer is a performance capability that results specifically from the methods by which information is coded into the brain (Steele and Penhune 2010; Becker et al.; Lin et al.).

Chapter 4

The Role of the Procedural Memory System

Recall that data stored in the procedural memory system is accessed without the need for conscious thought or intention. Research, extrapolation, and our own real-world operational experiences strongly suggest that this automatic access of information is, in fact, precisely what occurs when actions are performed under the effects of the stress response (Schwabe et al. 2010).

Examples abound of the operational impacts of what are sometimes referred to as *training scars*. These consist of nonsensical actions that are performed operationally under stress. Examples include officers handing their firearms to attackers after fighting successfully to retain them, releasing suspects they have physically subdued because the suspect "taps out," reholstering their weapons in the midst of lethal encounters, and picking up spent shell casings or empty magazines during gun battles. The term "training scar" is used to describe these types of actions when they are repetitively performed during training either in response to a stimulus or in sequence with other operationally required actions.

None of the actions that fall into this category are things that any reasonable human being would do after applying cognitive or decision-making processes to these situations. Nevertheless, knowledgeable, professionally trained individuals do perform them with stunning regularity. This results from unintentional, unconscious access, retrieval, and activation of the neural-networks that comprise performance of these actions. Performance is usually

43

based on either receipt of a stimulus, contextual presentation, or as part of a repetitively rehearsed sequence. Because performance of these actions is often associative or contextual and relates either to a stimulus or environment, factors relating to associative learning processes are likely among the issues that bear primary responsibility for their development. Furthermore, since access, retrieval, and subsequent performance of the action are not associated with a conscious process (and sometimes are not even remembered following the incident), we can surmise that these neural-networks are almost certainly stored within the long-term procedural memory system.

Information stored in the procedural and declarative long-term memory systems is located in different geographic areas of the brain and also accessible via separate pathways (Wolf 2010; Kassardjian et al. 2005). There is even documentation of people suffering from amnesia who do not have the ability to store or access declarative memories but are able to both access preexisting procedural memories and also formulate new ones, albeit without conscious awareness that this learning has occurred. These memories typically manifest either in response to stimuli or as part of the performance of a sequence (Schacter 1987). This suggests that, during the stress response, the skills stored within the procedural memory system are the skills that will be performed, regardless of what information may be contained within the short-term and declarative memory systems.

For example, imagine a student who is repetitively verbally told to drop magazines on the ground while reloading his or her weapon during a real-world shooting. The student fully understands this policy and is made to take a written test to ensure and document his or her cognitive understanding of it. This same student, despite his or her cognitive knowledge of the correct procedure, will most likely still retain magazines during an actual gunfight rather than drop them on the ground if he or she always retains magazines during physical training.

The reason for this is that the neural-network correlating to magazine retention is what exists within his or her procedural memory system. Under high levels of stress, the information and procedures in the declarative and short-term memory systems are far less likely to be accessed, retrieved, and performed than those in procedural memory. In fact, the hormone releases within the brain that occur as a result of stressful encounters act as a "switch" that highly favors the procedural memory system (Schwabe et al. 2010).

The important objective, then, for firearms and tactical instructors is to build into students' procedural memory systems the networks of skills, knowledge, contexts, judgments, and stimulus responses necessary to prevail during lethal encounters. Placing skills and knowledge within a student's short-term memory is of minimal benefit for performance under extreme levels of stress, even if that information is still present when recall is required. Similarly, long-term retention of skills or knowledge that will be applied operationally during high-stress events is likely to provide little, if any, operational benefit if it is retained solely within the declarative memory system.

Chapter 5

How Information Is Consolidated
Into the Procedural Memory System

We have presented our hypothesis that the primary objective of firearms and tactical training should be to develop neural-networks to encode applicable information in the procedural memory system. Therefore, it is important to understand how this process (sometimes generally referred to as *consolidation*) occurs. Although modern neuroscience and psychology cannot currently provide a definitive explanation, an ever-growing body of research on the subject offers some clues. The latest generally accepted model specific to motor skills performance involves a multiphase learning process that begins with a short period of fast acquisition followed by a long phase of slow consolidation, acquisition, and improvement (Kleim et al. 2004; Criscimagna-Hemminger and Shadmehr 2004; Ma et al. 2011). Specific to formulating a new skill or memory for the purposes discussed in this book, the process is divisible into four general areas: acquisition, stabilization, consolidation/transfer, and enhancement.

Acquisition (Fast)

The first phase of acquiring new knowledge, specifically knowledge related to physical skill performance, is initial acquisition. For acquisition to occur, the information must first get past the brain's filter and enter the short-term memory system. For skill-based learning, this information appears to be primarily distributed between the striatum and cerebellum (Kleim et al. 2004). When goals and associations are involved, the hippocampus also plays a key role, even with respect to motor skills (Colon-Cesario et al. 2006; McClelland

47

et al. 1994). The most effective, tried and true method for initial acquisition is repetition, particularly for physical motor skills (Shumway-Cooke and Woollacott 2012; Lee at al. 2012). Repeated skill performance repetitively fires the neurons involved, which begins the formation of a memory trace (Jensen 2008).

Stabilization (Fast)

Once initial acquisition has occurred, even though the information now exists within the short-term memory system, it is far from stable. In fact, research suggests that newly acquired information is inherently unstable and can easily be lost completely for at least ten minutes following the process of initial acquisition. This is probably because the protein synthesis necessary for the formation of a memory trace within the short-term memory system does not begin until approximately ten minutes have passed (Criscimagna-Hemminger and Shadmehr 2008).

If no disruptions occur during this time period, the memory gains some degree of stability, but it still appears highly vulnerable to disruption and interference *within short-term memory* for at least five hours (Shadmehr and Brashers-Krug 1997; Mirman and Spivey 2001). For training development purposes, it takes at least *twenty-four hours* before a newly acquired memory is relatively safe from interference or disruption, due to completion of the initial phases of consolidation and transfer of the information into long-term memory (Santini et al. 2001; Brashers-Krug et al. 1995; Shadmehr et al. 1995).

Consolidation/Transfer (Slow)

Consolidation of highly polished, expert-level motor skills performance is a long, multiphasic process that can span decades (Ericsson et al. 1993;

Jensen 2008). However, for the practical purposes of tactical training system development, the most critical phases of consolidation are those that initially code the information into the long-term procedural memory system, allowing both long-term retention and access under high levels of stress. It is a critical point for trainers to understand that only *after* a memory trace has developed within the short-term memory system can it be consolidated and transferred into long-term memory.

This consolidation involves changing the physical location within the brain where the memory is stored (Kassardjian et al. 2005). It also involves the performance of multiple biological and chemical processes (protein synthesis, for example) at the destination site in order to support development of a memory trace at that location (Kleim et al. 2004; Colon-Cesario et al. 2006; Ma et al. 2011; Criscimagna-Hemminger and Shadmehr 2008; Sakai et al. 1998).

The initial process of consolidation is the transfer of information from the location of the short-term memory system to the location of the long-term memory system (McClelland et al. 1994; Robertson et al. 2005; Steele and Penhune 2010; Kleim et al. 2004). This occurs gradually between five and twenty-four hours after the initial acquisition is completed (Santini et al 2001; Brashers-Krug et al. 1995; Shadmehr et al. 1995).

The process of the consolidation and transfer appears to be multiphasic, even for a relatively simple memory. Separate phases may happen at different time periods within this five- to twenty-four-hour window of initial consolidation. Different parts of the memory (for example, the goal of a skill versus the physical movements involved in a skill) appear to be transferred through different neurological processes at different times (Robertson 2009).

It is also noteworthy for instructors, trainers, and curriculum/training developers that while consolidation is essential for operationally relevant learning to occur, the actual process itself inhibits a student's ability to recall the information during the time period when the information is actively being consolidated (Steidl et al. 2006). In other words, a student's ability to recall information or perform a skill will be negatively affected for approximately twenty-four hours after training has been completed. Furthermore, requiring a student to access this information and/or perform the skill during this twenty-four hour period may negatively affect the brain's ability to effectively move the information to long-term memory.

Late Learning/Enhancement (Slow)

After information has been transferred into the procedural memory system, later stages of learning can then occur. These later stages of postconsolidation learning are what facilitate refinement and/or enhancement of the skill or memory (Ericsson et al. 1993; Steele and Penhune 2010). This process can continue for decades if the objective is attainment of expert-level performance (Ericsson et al. 1993).[2]

---

[2] The initial consolidation from short-term memory to long-term is a different process, utilizing different chemical and biological processes, than manipulation and reconsolidation of information that already exists in long-term memory (Colon-Cesario et al. 2006). In turn, the reconsolidation associated with learning enhancement may have less of an effect on a student's ability to recall or perform for the (roughly) twenty-four hour period following training than is produced via the initial process of consolidation from short-term memory.

Chapter 6

Factors Contributing to Neural-Network Development and Consolidation Into Procedural Memory That Can Be Influenced by Instructors and Trainers

Training systems for tactical applications should be designed in such a way that information and skills are placed effectively into short-term memory and then transferred to the appropriate long-term memory system for operational application. To date, we have identified twelve distinct and relevant factors that instructors and training-program developers can influence directly. They are priming, repetition, observation, emotional connection, stress, waking offline time, sleep, exercise, interleaved practice, interference, mixing memory system objectives, and time of day. In this section, we identify and examine each of these factors with respect to how they impact learning, retention, and retrieval. We also discuss the conceptual application of these factors in order to facilitate the development of more effective training.

Priming (Preexposure)

The first step to effectively developing neural-networks in short-term memory is to ensure that the information being presented passes through the brain's filtering system and arrives in the short-term memory system (Jensen 2008). Preexposure to the information, sometimes called priming, is one of the most effective ways to ensure that this occurs consistently across a group of students with a broadly mixed set of life experiences.

The human brain is designed to recognize patterns. Much of the information that is not retained in memory for the purposes discussed in this book still leaves some manner of residual neural imprint. Once a set of neurons is fired (even if the information is never stabilized or consolidated), the brain may be quicker to recognize, accept as important, and filter out extraneous information or other distractions if this same pattern of neurons is ever fired again (Jensen 2008; Wolfe 2010; McRae and Hetherington).

The importance of this is that critical information and skills should first be presented to, and practiced by, students purely as a primer. In other words, the skills should be presented and practiced with no expectation that students will understand, learn, or otherwise retain any of the information. The objective of priming sessions is not to teach but rather to create a clear pathway for the information to flow into the short-term memory system. This will occur when the information is presented again during a later teaching session. Based upon our observations in delivering training, this teaching session should most ideally occur between twenty-four and forty-eight hours after the priming session is complete, although longer delays of a week or more have still shown observable benefits.

The advantages of priming are threefold for firearms and tactics instructors. First, it helps limit the negative effects of progressive interference (discussed later in detail) and therefore increases the efficiency and effectiveness of the actual teaching session by defining a more specifically targeted neural-network for acquisition, consolidation, or enhancement. While less time efficient relative to *presenting* a volume of information, this technique is far more time efficient for *learning* the information presented. Therefore, priming reduces the overall teaching, training, and practice time required to produce the same level of proficiency.

Second, priming helps level the playing field with regards to variance in student retention and performance during group instruction. It evens the pace of training, increases instructional consistency, and increases the effectiveness of the overall program of instruction. It is common to have a mixed variety of backgrounds and experiences within any group of students. Some are likely to have existing experiences and prior learning similar to the information being presented. This enables them to quickly and efficiently absorb and retain the new information because the training largely utilizes pre-existing neural-networks. In neurological terms, this means that very few new connections between neurons actually need to be made to facilitate learning for these students. From a broader instructional view, students in this category can sometimes drive the pace of group instruction, leaving other students behind. Alternatively, they can easily become bored in the early phases of training. As a result, they can sometimes stop paying attention, fail to pick up key concepts, and therefore quickly fall behind as training progresses.

Consistent use of priming throughout the teaching process mitigates these concerns by helping students with no prior experience or incorrect prior experience to progress faster. It also facilitates the capability for initially advanced students to focus on fine-tuning skills (late-stage learning/enhancement) during early instructional sessions. Priming also ensures that the neural-networks associated with any information that does happen to be new to these advanced or experienced students are primed prior to the actual teaching session. This prevents them missing important information due to lack of attention.

Other students have backgrounds and experiences that directly conflict with the information being presented. They usually understand the information presented and may retain it easily within declarative memory; however, different neural-networks than those intended via the program of instruction may already be associated with the same stimuli, contexts, and skill sequences contained within the new training program. Performance of skills taught will be difficult, and the learning process resulting in procedural consolidation will be impeded.

These students require a slow, deliberate approach to presenting material, because completely new, competing associative networks and responses to stimuli or actions in sequence must be developed. Priming is the first step in accomplishing this process. Without it, achieving consistent performance results with students who fall into this category is a challenge.

Other students are true beginners. These students may have had no previous exposure to similar subject material and may have never previously developed applicable neural-networks within relevant parts of the brain. For example, a student with no athletic background may have developed very few stimulus-based visuomotor skills. Students in this category also require a slow, deliberate approach to instruction for optimal results. Priming is the first step to effectively and efficiently training them, as it helps ensure that all required information is processed into the short-term memory system. These students have no competing stimulus responses, contextual associations, or sequences within their procedural memory system. Once the appropriate networks are developed, they have the potential to become highly skilled in a relatively short time period.

Third, priming helps to limit the effects of the fear emotion that is often induced in beginning students during their initial handling of firearms and ammunition or exposure to tactical skill sets. Through both priming and a process of gradual exposure to weapons and weapons-handling skills over time (particularly in the initial stages of training), students' natural fear of the tools and/or subject matter is significantly reduced. Therefore, when important information and skills are introduced, the brain chemicals which result from fear are far below maximum levels or nonexistent. This minimizes or eliminates the harmful effects of information extinction and consolidation blocking. It also limits the negative stimulus and contextual associations that can be byproducts of the hormones that result from fear.

Repetition

Repetition is the single most important factor affecting fundamental motor skill development and is the basis of connectionist (Hebbian) learning theory (Lee at al. 2012). Hebb's Law can be summarized as "The neurons that fire together wire together." This occurs through a series of biological and chemical processes in the brain. Repetitive firing of a neural-network improves connectivity between the neurons involved. This, in turn, produces a memory trace, which results in learning via information retention (Jensen 2008).

Observation

It is well known that humans learn effectively by example and adapt their behavior to emulate those around them. This is sometimes called observational learning and is generally accepted to be the most effective form of learning (Van Gog et al. 2009). Recent neurological research has demonstrated that the human brain contains structures (or a system) sometimes referred to as *mirror neurons* (Bates 2009; Kilner et al. 2009). These neurons take the emulative properties of the brain beyond social adaptation and provide a neurological basis for replication of observed physical actions. Mirror neurons are physically a part of the actual neural-networks fired during physical action and are fired during both the physical performance of an action and during observation of that action without physical performance (Buccino and Riggio 2006; Agnew et al. 2008).[3]

---

[3] There is evidence that mirror neurons are even capable of firing when the performance of an action is heard rather than observed, as the existence of mirror neurons has been confirmed in persons who have been blind since birth. However, this effect seems to be limited to actions that are familiar to and have been previously performed by the listener and only about 15 percent of the total system appears to respond to audio only (Bates 2009; Buccino and Riggio 2006).

Research demonstrates that both significantly increased learning performance and improved early consolidation into procedural memory (particularly of motor skills) occur when the actions are both performed *and* observed repetitively during initial training/skill acquisition (Stefan et al. 2005; Van Gog et al. 2009; Zhang et al. 2011). These effects appear to have two causes. The first is that observation of the motion being performed refires the same neural-networks that are fired during actual physical performance (Buccino and Riggio 2006; Agnew et al. 2008). In other words, observing the performance of an action is at least partially the neurological equivalent to physically performing the action. This means that observing the performance of an action equates to the physical performance of additional repetitions of that action, albeit with a significantly reduced physical requirement. Furthermore, if the actions being observed are performed with technical perfection, the neurons that correspond to technically correct execution are the ones that will be repetitively fired within the student's brain.

The second cause (primarily associated with the improved procedural consolidation produced by action observation in conjunction with physical training) is that mirror neurons do *not* appear to primarily be located within the short-term memory system. Rather, the mirror neurons associated with motor skill performance appear to be located within the motor cortex—a primary location of the procedural memory system (Stefan et al. 2005). This means that what occurs neurologically during action observation is most likely repetitive firing of the neurons that are located within the procedural memory space, *not* within the short-term memory space. Therefore, observation may in fact jump-start formation of a memory trace at its ultimate destination (long-term procedural memory space) by initiating the protein synthesis and other biological/chemical processes necessary for the permanent storage of the memory at the destination location. The result is increased efficiency in the information transfer that occurs during the early process of consolidation, as the memory trace network at the destination site is already in development when the transfer of the memory from the short-term system is initiated.

The mirror neuron system's effectiveness is not limited to observation of live performance of the action. Dynamic visualization utilizing video is also effective. This is true even if the actions are performed by a machine or animation approximating human action (Van Gog et al. 2009). It is also noteworthy that the specific hand or limb being observed correlates directly to the mirror neurons that are activated. In other words, the specific limb being observed is the limb for which the memory trace in the motor cortex will be formed through observation (Schmeulof and Zohary 2006). This makes the requirement for observation specific to a side when applying this tool to teaching certain firearms-related motor skills. In other words, a separate visualization performance or training aid will be necessary for students who are learning to perform a skill with their left hands than will be necessary for students performing the same skill with their right hands.

To employ observational learning effectively, there are several things to consider. First, research suggests that preexisting experiences are a significant contributor to mirror-neuron performance (Catmur et al. 2008; Bates 2009). In other words, activation of the mirror-neuron system depends on previous experience utilizing the neurons involved in the action. For trainers and curriculum developers, this means that observational learning drills should be incorporated following, not prior to, initial skills training. This does not mean that a skill should not be demonstrated or viewed prior to practice (this is a critical component of teaching skill performance); it *does* mean that observation exercises intended for the specific purpose of enhancing consolidation should be conducted after the physical portion of the training session is complete. Also, the correct length of time for viewing repetitive skill performance appears to be in the vicinity of seven minutes (Zhang et al. 2011).

Second, one of the biggest contributing factors to effective mirror-neuron activation is identification with the *intent* of a goal-directed action. It is not enough to simply view an action. To achieve the maximum learning effect, the action must be viewed with the intent to replicate performance of the action in order to achieve a specific goal (Van Gog et al. 2009; Buccino and Riggio 2006).

Third, there is evidence that once a skill has been well learned, visual examples and observational learning no longer contribute to improvement and may even hamper additional learning or enhancement—this is due to a phenomenon called the expertise-reversal effect. As a student's skill performance approaches an expert level, further observational learning exercises specific to that skill are unlikely to induce positive results and may actually be detrimental (Van Gog et al. 2009).[4, 5]

Emotional Connection

Emotions, including fear, stress, anger, and happiness largely result from differing chemical balances within specific parts of the brain (Jensen 2008).

---

[4] Training-based utilization of mirror neurons and the powerful effects of observational learning are not limited to motor skills alone. The benefits appear to also extend to cognitive tasks, decision-making, and problem solving. It is important to note that effective use of observational learning for these applications can only be accomplished with advanced students who already possess, at an expert level, the full body of skills, knowledge, or other information necessary to accomplish the task or solve the problem (Van Gog et al. 2009).

[5] Most athletes and many trainers in the tactical realm discuss the benefits of visualization and mental rehearsal. While outside the scope of this research, it is probable that one of the benefits of visualization is in fact activation of the mirror-neuron system.

We have previously demonstrated that learning, according to the connectionist (Hebbian) model, involves chemical, biological, and physical changes between brain cells. Because the actual process of learning is heavily dependent upon chemical reactions that occur at the physical location where the information is stored within the brain, the emotional state of the brain (determined by the levels of various chemicals in specific areas) is a critical factor in optimizing learning success (Jensen 2008; Wolfe 2010; Steidl et al. 2006; Blanchard et al. 2001; Duncko et al. 2009; Thomas and LaBar 2008).

Depending upon the specific emotion(s) being experienced, the level of the emotion(s), the specific type of information or skill being learned, and the phase of learning that is occurring, students' learning performances in specific skill areas can be either greatly enhanced or greatly decreased by the emotions that they experience before, during, and after the training period. It is also worth noting that there appears to be at least a partially symbiotic relationship between emotions and learning. The development of neural-networks, specifically within the procedural system, appears to change the actual physical circuits through which emotions are expressed (Blanchard et al. 2001). In other words, training that implants information into the procedural memory system has the potential to affect students' future emotional responses, particularly those relating to the subject matter being trained.

Details of the causes of, effects of, and relationships between emotions and learning are far from being fully understood. However, our limited knowledge does provide some useful insight for trainers. Understanding how differing emotions effect students' abilities to learn, retain, and recall information is important because it can impact methods of training delivery as well as the structure and design of training systems.

There are two common emotional responses that are within the purview of trainers to anticipate, control, and affect. These are fear and emotional arousal (defined as a nonfear emotional response resulting in a chemical change within the brain [hormone release]). The latter can be thought of as an intense feeling (love, joy, hate, affection, etc.) that results from a presented stimulus.

Fear

While all emotions can impact learning, fear has the unique ability to almost instantaneously form permanent associative and/or contextual memory traces through chemical action, usually relating specifically to the source of the fear (Krugers et al. 2011). Fear-related chemicals within the brain can also disrupt the brain's ability to learn (more specifically to acquire, stabilize, and consolidate) information (Thomas and LaBar 2008). These chemicals can also inhibit recall capability as well as promote the extinction of existing information (Krugers et al. 2011). Fear-related chemicals also appear to limit the brain's ability to perform learning transfer and develop new associations across stimuli or environments (Becker et al.).

When students experience the specific emotion of fear in a training environment, they are simply not physiologically capable of learning effectively in the traditional sense of acquiring and retaining information. However, a student's strong fear emotion during training *does* have the ability to almost instantaneously create associative connections between actions and stimuli, stimuli and environments, and so on—connections that may become more or less permanent (Krugers et al. 2011).

It appears that this phenomenon of creating near-instantaneous permanent memory for very specific associations, contextual relationships, and experiences most likely occurs due to an intense chemical reaction within a very specific part of the brain that is specifically involved in associative learning.

The result can be thought of as a chemical "burn" inside the brain, resulting in the formation of a permanent memory trace in an area that is likely normally utilized as short-term memory space, but that is transformed into a part of the long-term procedural memory system.

Alternatively, or perhaps additionally, the changed chemical levels may cause the generation of new neurons in the hippocampus (Rauchs et al. 2011). This, in turn, may result in or contribute to the long-term retention of the burn-like symptoms that appear to function as a part of procedural memory. In any case, the functional result is that if fear related chemical levels are high enough, this "permanent" memory trace can be formed after only a single instance of firing the neural circuit. This effect contributes to the overconsolidation of traumatic experiences that may in turn contribute to an increased predilection for psychological aftereffects to traumatic incidents such as post-traumatic stress-related injuries (Krugers et al. 2011).

Because of this effect, fear in a training environment can be an extremely powerful tool to instantaneously create permanent associative memories. It can also instantaneously create near-permanent training scars or operationally harmful associations that can result in unwanted, involuntary responses to stimuli or reactions to contexts or environments. Furthermore, high levels of fear in a training environment are likely to inhibit other learning processes and may result in the loss of previously learned information, particularly if that information has not yet been fully stabilized and/or consolidated into one of the long-term memory systems.

Because of these potential effects, creating a fear response in students should generally be carefully avoided during training sessions unless the training objective is to formulate a very specific and unmistakable association that will be purposefully introduced during an instructor-induced fear response.

Furthermore, fear during training should be avoided altogether if students have not fully developed consolidated procedural memories for the skills and procedures that they will utilize during the training session. Otherwise, instructors may unwittingly create near-permanent training scars. Furthermore, the training scars may only manifest during performance under the effects of the stress response, making it next to impossible to diagnose and correct them in a training environment.

There are two common situations in which the fear response is generated in students during firearms and tactical training. The first is during the initial training period(s), when students are uncomfortable with the tools and/or subject matter and may be irrationally afraid of the object(s) or even the topic itself. The second is during scenario-based training, when attempts are made to intentionally replicate the operational effects of the sympathetic nervous system and stress response during simulations.

When students experience the fear emotion, particularly during their initial training and handling of a weapon, they are unlikely to learn what the instructor intends to teach them. They are also likely to develop training scars (even after just a few minutes of training) that may take years to correct, if they can be corrected at all. Similarly, when students who do not possess the full battery of consolidated skill sets necessary to perform successfully are placed into scenario-based training environments, improper skill performance and training scars in the form of inappropriate or dangerous decisions, responses to stimuli, or contextual associations may inadvertently become permanently formed procedural memory traces. Therefore, full-fledged, scenario-based training that may produce this emotional response should not be introduced until students are fully prepared to succeed. This will involve a progressive training and evaluation process that ensures that they have already consolidated the appropriate skills and responses into procedural memory.

Note that procedural memory development may also affect future emotional responses. This means that procedurally consolidated skills may be a kind of "antidote" for fear. In our personal operational experience, we have observed that minimally trained security and military personnel often experience extreme effects of fear and stress during their first exposure to combat and sometimes also during exposure to simulator training if they have not previously developed the skill set necessary to perform within the training scenario. Even in training environments, these effects have included such actions as personnel diving headfirst into walls.

In contrast, highly trained personnel who have progressively been thoroughly trained, including the use of extensive, scenario-based force-on-force simulations, often report experiencing something more aptly described as a euphoric calm, even during their first exposure to combat (despite experiencing remembered effects of the sympathetic nervous system). While by no means conclusive, this is anecdotal support for the hypothesis that developing *appropriate* procedural memories for the operational environment with well-designed training systems may limit the impacts of emotional effects during critical incidents. This may also mitigate the negative long-term emotional and psychological effects that can manifest as by-products of such experiences.

While chemicals of fear appear to have relatively unique effects on the brain's learning activities, the fact that fear's chemical levels and mixtures *have* an effect on the brain's learning processes is not unique. Fear is an easy emotion to specifically identify, quantify, and artificially produce in a controlled environment for the purposes of scientific study. Other specific emotional reactions are less easy to identify, and therefore to study; however, other emotions still result from chemical changes inside the brain and therefore are still recognizable as emotions in a laboratory environment (Thomas and LaBar 2008). Furthermore, while other emotions may not be as easily identifiable for scientific study, they *can* generally be distinguished as being different from fear. There is a substantial and growing body of scientific research that suggests a strong correlation between the level of nonfear emotional arousal (both during and following training sessions) and the effectiveness of the brain's learning process (Jensen 2008; Steidl et al. 2006; McIntyre and Roozendaal 2007).

Emotional Arousal (Related to Stimuli)

One area that has received a significant amount of study is that surrounding the effects of unspecified (nonfear) emotional arousal both during and following training. This state of emotional arousal often is induced during scientific research through intentionally produced interaction with stimuli that generate a measurable (nonfear) emotional reaction in test subjects. The effects of this stimulus-related emotional arousal have been examined both when the increased levels of emotion occur during training and also when they occur following the training period.

Results of these studies indicate that emotional arousal during training impairs some of the initial learning and acquisition process. However, counterintuitively, the same emotional arousal that impairs the initial learning process also improves long-term retention of the same information (Steidl et al. 2006). Specifically, consolidation of long-term memories is what the chemical mixture created by nonfear emotional arousal improves (McIntyre and Roozendaal 2007). This effectively means that an overall instructional environment (with regards to regulating and inducing student emotional response) that consistently produces better performance results at the end of the instructional period may actually result in *less* effective long-term performance and information retention than an environment that produces worse performance results either during or shortly after the training period.

Emotional arousal induced after the training period has ended (during the stabilization and consolidation processes) has also been shown to have a consistent and positive effect on learning (Steidl et al. 2006). These effects are increased when the initial learning/acquisition of the information occurred while the student was also in an emotionally aroused state (Steidl et al. 2006).

The takeaway for instructors, trainers, and curriculum developers is that helping students establish an emotional connection with the subject matter, the objectives of the actions being performed in training, or even the context in which the instruction is occurring can significantly improve long-term learning and retention. This requires no additional investment of training time or significant resources. Additionally, following up instructional periods with experiences and/or stimuli that generate an emotional response (even if the emotions are not directly related to the period of instruction or subject matter) is likely to enhance these effects further. This can result in even greater levels of long-term retention and performance without increasing the amount of time spent training or practicing.

It is important that stimuli, contexts, activities, or other tools utilized to induce emotional responses do *not* produce a fear response. Similar (moderate) levels of emotional arousal can either enhance learning or inhibit learning. The deciding factor is whether or not the emotion is fear (Thomas and LaBar 2008).

A 2009 study discovered that dopamine (pleasure) receptor activation is an important factor in processing spatial information that is dependent upon the hippocampus, which is generally responsible for associative learning (Pennartz et al. 2009). This means that if a pleasurable emotion can be initiated within students during learning that requires spatial awareness, their physiological ability to process and retain the information may be improved. Examples could include task completion, positive reinforcement, enjoyable experiences, a social reward based on success, and pleasurable physical, visual, or audio stimuli.

It is also worth noting however that once a student becomes intimately familiar with the context surrounding the training, the positive consolidation effects from emotional arousal during and after the training periods are reduced (McIntyre and Roozendaal 2007). This means that the training environment and any specific emotion-producing contextual associations should be varied as training progresses in order to maintain maximum possible benefit. If logistical limitations make this problematic, careful planning and curriculum design should be done to maximize the predictable consolidation effects produced by the resources that are available. This can be accomplished by prioritizing training material and using emotional learning to enhance consolidation of the most important operational concepts.

Stress

The effects of stimulus-related emotional arousal on the learning process appear to be directly related to student stress levels, another external factor that instructors can control and/or influence in training environments (McIntyre and Roozendaal 2007). For the purposes of this book, we will divide stress in a training environment into two different categories. The first is low-level stress, which physiologically results in small to moderate amounts of chemicals being released in the brain. The second is high-level stress, during which large amounts of chemicals are released. Studies have shown that stress improves memory and learning performance (Duncko et al. 2007). They have also shown that stress inhibits these same factors (Kim et al. 2001; Becker et al.). The critical factor determining whether stress improves or hinders learning appears to be the level of stress and therefore the amount of chemicals involved (McIntyre and Roozendaal 2007; Duncko et al. 2009).

Stress (Low Levels)

Low-level stress can be induced either physically (such as with a minimal level of physical discomfort or performance of physical activity) or mentally (such as with the imposition of deadlines or standards). There is a well-documented, affirmative link between low to moderate stress and improved learning performance. However, recent research has revealed some details regarding this link that are of particular interest to tactical trainers and curriculum designers.

First, it appears that the positive effects of stress on learning performance are not the same across genders. The effects appear to be much more prevalent for male students than they are for female students (Duncko 2007; Wolf 2003). Therefore, curricula that is designed to use low-level stress as a learning-enhancement tool may produce differing or possibly even opposite effects in female students. As a result, for optimal learning effectiveness, it may be advantageous for neurophysiological reasons to separate genders during some specific periods of instruction and to design separate learning modules for each gender if the instructional method for the topic involves the use of low-level stress to enhance learning results.[6]

---

[6] This possibility of considering gender separation for some periods of instruction is not related to training that involves intentional inducement of stressful conditions to simulate a combat/operational environment and prepare/condition the student to perform under the physiological effects of the sympathetic nervous system. This is solely focused on maximizing each student's neurological ability to acquire and consolidate information to the procedural memory system in the most effective and efficient manner possible by accounting for scientifically documented neurological differences between how the two genders stabilize and consolidate information.

The second item of note is that low levels of stress appear to enhance (male) learning performance by streamlining the processing of information within the brain (Duncko et al. 2009). This effect appears to be produced, at least in part, by an enhancement of the brain's initial filtering process, which prevents information deemed unimportant from entering into working/short-term memory (Duncko et al. 2009). This effect makes it all the more important for instructors to use the priming technique to introduce every mission-critical technique or concept, thereby preventing important information from being filtered out by the effects of low-level stress rather than being coded more effectively into long-term memory.

Finally, there appears to be a very strong link between the positive learning effects of low-level stress and the emotional connection that a student has with the acquisition of the related information. According to a study conducted by McIntyre and Roozendaal, "Extensive evidence indicates that stress hormones released from the adrenal glands are critically involved in memory consolidation of emotionally arousing experiences" (2007). According to their research, training-associated emotional arousal is a requirement in order for stress hormones to increase memory consolidation. This means that effective utilization of low-level stress as a training aid may require pairing with the use of emotionally arousing experiences or stimuli specific to the training topic, making the application of emotional learning even more critical.

Low-level stress has the potential to be a useful tool for increasing long-term training efficiency and effectiveness. However, due to the specificity regarding its positive effects, using it to enhance consolidation is something that should be carefully considered before implementation is attempted. It should only be utilized as part of a complete, intentionally designed, learning system.

Low-level stress is not a training tool that should be haphazardly applied.

Stress (High Levels—the Sympathetic Nervous System)

The second category of stress for the purposes of this book is high-level stress. This is generally characterized by the release of high levels of chemicals, including cortisol and epinephrine, into the brain (Duncko et al. 2009; Krugers et al. 2011). In our personal experience, high levels of stress can also be accompanied by activation of the sympathetic (fight or flight) nervous system.

Practically, high-level stress performs much the same way as fear in a learning environment. It produces abnormally high levels of chemicals within the brain that interfere with the brain's ability to learn—with the notable exception of very specific, contextual associations that generally relate directly to the environment or the source of the stress (Krugers et al. 2011; Duncko et al. 2009; Becker et al.). If the stress is high enough to activate the sympathetic nervous system, additional physiological effects can occur that not only preclude learning, but also preclude the recall and use of information that is not already contained within the procedural memory system (Schwabe et al. 2010). Furthermore, stress chemicals can inhibit the processes that are responsible for the development of future learning-transfer performance (Becker et al.).

Therefore, intentional introduction of high levels of stress should not be done in a training environment where *learning* skills or information is the training objective. Performance of skills and utilization of information under high levels of stress are indispensable components of a tactical program of instruction, but these should be introduced only *after* the full body of information required for successful performance has already been coded into procedural memory. Care should also be taken not to accidentally create harmful contextual or stimulus associations or decision patterns through careless training development.

Off-Line Time (Waking)

Although somewhat counterintuitive, one of the most important factors affecting stabilization and consolidation to procedural memory is "downtime," sometimes scientifically referred to as *off-line time*. This is defined as a time period following the training or learning session during which the learner's brain is *not* consciously involved in accessing, processing or using the information or skills.

Recall that the process that results in the long-term retention of information is multiphasic, consisting of initial acquisition, stabilization within short-term memory, consolidation and transfer to long-term memory, and finally, late learning/enhancement within long-term memory. Also remember that a student's ability to recall information and perform skills is inhibited during the time period(s) when both the stabilization and consolidation/transfer processes are occurring.

Information and/or skills are initially acquired as a result of active sensory input and the repetitive firing of neural-networks, initiating the chemical and physical changes that equate to learning and memory formation. However, much of the actual process of learning not only *can* occur during time periods outside of the actual training time itself, but actually *must* occur outside of the actual training period. Stabilization, consolidation, and enhancement are all dependent upon multiple processes that occur exclusively during both day and night off-line learning (Robertson et al. 2005).

Depending on the type of learning and memory systems involved, different processes and neural-networks are used in off-line learning (Ma et al.

2011). However, there is overwhelming scientific evidence that not only do the processes of stabilization and consolidation/transfer depend upon off-line time, but a student's performance ability can also increase from the level attained in training after a period of off-line time (Della-Maggiore 2005; Song et al. 2007). In fact, some scientists have actually defined consolidation as learning improvement that occurs after off-line time has elapsed, without additional instruction or practice (Steele and Penhune 2010).

The reason that this performance improvement occurs, specifically during the early stages of skills learning, is that during off-line time the brain actually refires the same neural circuits that were fired during the training session (Albert et al. 2009). In other words, the same neurons that are fired with each repetition during training are fired again in sequence by the brain when it is "off-line," without conscious awareness on the part of the student. These repeated firings increase the strength of the neural connections. This equivalent of increased repetition does *not* seem to occur after a practice session for skills that have already been learned; it appears to be a phenomenon specific to new learning (Albert et al. 2009).

The importance of this knowledge for instructors is in recognizing that more instruction time and more practice time do not necessarily equate to increased learning or better student performance. Quite to the contrary, the opposite is often true. Too much instruction and/or practice within too short a time period can be detrimental to both learning and performance (Ericsson et al. 1993). For students to learn efficiently and effectively, they *must* be provided the off-line time necessary to stabilize, consolidate, and transfer the information and skills into long-term memory.

During this off-line time, as the processes of transfer and consolidation are in progress, the students' ability to recall the information is inhibited.

Therefore, it is important that this time period not be utilized for assessments of performance or training effectiveness. Testing, evaluation, or other forced recall during this period will not only provide inaccurate information regarding operational performance potential, it will also impede the learning process, thus negatively affecting long-term retention.

Off-line time should be at least twenty-four hours. This is the minimum amount of time necessary for information to be consolidated enough to resist either being lost or interfered with as a result of new information being presented (Santini et al. 2001; Brashers-Krug et al. 1995; Shadmehr et al. 1995). This must also include a sleep period that, along with sleep-associated off-line brain functionality, is a critical factor related to improving the efficiency and effectiveness of learning performance.

Sleep

Another tremendously important factor that greatly impacts both learning in general and consolidation to long-term memory in particular is sleep. It is well known that well-rested students perform better in the classroom (Jensen 2008). This is both unsurprising and intuitive, as the mind and body require rest and fuel to function effectively. However, sleep also provides another, less intuitively obvious yet critically important learning function: sleep consolidation (Fischer et al. 2005; Rauchs et al. 2011).

Sleep consolidation is similar in concept to off-line consolidation and in fact was generally considered to be the same thing until recently. While there is at present some disagreement within the scientific community as to the specifics (the underlying scientific study is ongoing), it is generally accepted that sleep and waking off-line time, while having similar benefits, actually facilitate different functions related to learning consolidation (Robertson 2009;

Albert et al. 2009; Song et al. 2007).

During an actual physical learning or practice session, all mechanisms associated with learning information or skills are engaged. After the practice session ends, however, this is no longer the case. Different parts of the information that ultimately comprise operational performance are consolidated off-line through different neurological processes that occur at different times (Cohen et al. 2005). Some of these processes appear to occur exclusively during waking periods; others occur just as exclusively during sleep (Cohen et al. 2005; Montgomery et al. 2008; Brown and Robertson 2007; Albert et al. 2009; Robertson et al. 2005). It is also of note that, similar to waking off-line consolidation, the effects of sleep consolidation appear to be limited to learning and do *not* occur after the practice of skills that have previously been learned and consolidated (Albert et al. 2009).

The primary benefit of sleep-based procedural consolidation for motor skills appears to be related to the goals and objectives of skill performance (Robertson 2009). This includes visuomotor skills such as targeting tasks (ocular focus, followed by physical action, based on feedback through visual stimuli). It is noteworthy for firearms instructors that ocular response appears to be more important for success than the physical motor response during the performance of targeting tasks (Maquet et al. 2003; Vickers 2007). The learning enhancements in this area that are produced by sleep appear to result from the replay and rehearsal (refiring of the utilized neural circuits) during sleep (Pennartz et al. 2009; Maquet et al. 2003). This, in effect, results in de facto additional repetition of these facets of the skill while the student is asleep.

The actual physical motion of the skill does not appear to be consolidated (defined here as improvement in performance without additional practice) to procedural memory during sleep (Song et al. 2007). However, there is nevertheless some evidence that the physical motion itself may still be stabilized and/or recovered (from interference or partial loss) (Brawn et al. 2010). It is important to note that these effects are specific to procedural consolidation. Sleep does appear to consolidate and improve performance for declarative (conscious and intentional recall and performance) motor skill memory (Lee et al. 2012; Cohen et al. 2005).

Sleep also appears to facilitate changes to certain aspects of brain chemistry that affect pattern-recognition capabilities and therefore can result in a type of unconscious analysis of existing data. This change can result in the development of novel inferences and new connections between data points that were not previously recognized (Montgomery et al. 2008). This function can enhance problem-solving capabilities and lends some scientific support to the concept of "sleeping on a problem" before making a decision. This effect (new connections and novel inferences) may be enhanced through the sleep-driven process of deleting data not recognized as valuable by the subconscious mind, thus effectively reducing the information clutter existing between important pieces of information (Rauchs et al. 2011; Fischer et al. 2005).

Finally, sleep also appears to accelerate improvements to decision-making and problem-solving abilities that can occur as a result of training (Kuriyama et al. 2008). It is likely that this improvement results from an increased level of neural plasticity that occurs during the sleep period (Kuriyama et al. 2008).

It is also noteworthy that the post-training period during which sleep provides the most benefit for the information presented during a particular lesson appears to be limited to approximately twelve hours (Fischer et al. 2005). The takeaway for trainers and curriculum developers is that if students do not receive a full sleep period within twelve hours of completing training during which initial acquisition/learning occurs, a significant amount of the potential for long-term retention may be lost.

Exercise

Moderate levels of exercise have been shown to improve students' learning abilities and overall performances (Jensen 2008). At least some of this improvement is produced via increased neurogenesis, particularly in the hippocampus (Rauchs et al. 2011). While hippocampal neurogenesis is not important for all learning, it appears to be critically important for associative and contextual learning as well as learning transfer or the ability to apply learning across varying stimuli (Becker et al.).

The lesson for trainers is that requiring the performance of physical exercise during the day (although not necessarily during training itself) is likely to increase students' learning retention, long-term skills performance, and learning-transfer abilities, particularly regarding those skills that relate to contextual association and stimulus response.

Interleaved Training (Judgment, Modification/Transfer, and Retention through Contextual Interference)

Traditional training methodology, particularly for firearms skills, utilizes the bulk of available training time with a teaching technique that is sometimes referred to as *blocked training*; in other words, learning and/or practicing the performance of a very specific skill that is known to the student in advance. The training is highly structured, the environment is sterile, and skills are presented and practiced in a very logical, progressive manner. Blocked-training methodology is widely used because it consistently produces the fastest measurable training-period performance improvement as well as the best end of training performance, particularly during a time-limited training period (hours or days) (Vickers 2007). Somewhat counterintuitively, however, blocked training does *not* produce optimal results for either long-term retention or operational performance (Vickers 2007; Cross et al. 2007). Instead, an approach called interleaved training, where learning and practice are conducted in a somewhat haphazard, chaotic manner, ultimately produces far better long-term retention and much better operational results (Vickers 2007; Cross et al. 2007; Lin et al.).

Contextual interference is a scientific term for the phenomenon that produces increased retention and performance from certain types of difficulties, chaos, and confusion during training and practice (Lin et al. 2009). It is important to recognize that these long-term benefits occur even though this approach produces *lower* measurable performance during the actual training period than blocked training does (Lin et al; Cross et al. 2007). Since this term is extremely confusing to the layperson, we will not use it again in this book. However, the concept, and the methods through which this effect can be employed to improve long-term and operational results are critical to understand. Appropriate exploitation of interleaved training techniques is one of the most powerful yet under utilized tools available to firearms and tactical trainers for improving operational results.

The most effective way to clearly define interleaved training is through the use of an example. Imagine working with a basketball player on fundamental skills. Each skill will be performed with fifteen repetitions. First, the player performs free throws. Next, the player performs three-point shots from the baseline right of the basket. Then, the player performs lay-ups from the right side, followed by lay-ups from the left side. Finally, the player practices ball handling. This is an example of blocked practice. The player knows before the drill begins exactly what skill they will be performing and under what conditions they will be performing it. Therefore, the player does not need to engage any brain function or memory other than what is necessary for the physical performance of the motor skill.

The physical motor skills developed through blocked practice are well polished, particularly when performed in a similarly sterile environment. However, if the environment, context, or conditions change, the performance ability for these skills is greatly affected. For example purposes, assume that a player trained in this manner is able to make 95 percent of the shots taken on a standards test given at the end of the practice period. A month later, this player may make 70 percent of the shots taken on the same test. In an actual game, the player may only make 40 percent of the shots.

Now assume another basketball player is working on fundamental skills. This player will perform the same number of overall repetitions during a practice period of the same length. However, the practice is structured very differently. The player doesn't know in advance what skills will be performed, at what location on the court they will be performed, or when they will be performed. Maybe the player isn't even told what skills to perform, but must choose one in response to a given situation or stimulus. At the conclusion of the training session, this player might only score 85 percent on the same standards test as the first player. However, when the test is administered a month later, this player scores 80 percent. During an actual game, this player makes 70 percent of the shots. Thus, though this second player exhibits significantly poorer test scores at the end of training than the first one does, he or she still ultimately retains a much higher level of skill and also is far better prepared to actually perform in competition.

	End-of-Training Test	Thirty-Day Test	Game Performance
Player One (Blocked)	95 percent	70 percent	40 percent
Player Two (Interleaved)	85 percent	80 percent	70 percent

Table 1

The example above is oversimplified, and the players as well as the percentages used are fictitious. However, the pattern of the performance results is not. They have been consistently demonstrated in research studies, confirming what Vickers calls the paradox of modern motor learning research (Vickers 2007). These results also mirror the results of our own experiences throughout several decades of delivering firearms and tactical training. Additional research is required to quantify specific standard and/or operational performance results in response to specific firearms and tactical training applications of interleaved learning and practice. (For more detailed information about previous athletic and sport-oriented operationally based research studies conducted in this area, we recommend starting with Chapter 9 of *Perception, Cognition, and Decision Training: The Quiet Eye in Action* by Joan Vickers.)

Applying these concepts to firearms and tactical training systems is somewhat counterintuitive when using the current paradigm because the existing structure usually measures success through end-of-training performance metrics. However, the neurological reasons for the superiority of interleaved training over blocked training in terms of improved retention and operational performance are relatively straightforward.

Improved Retention

The first effect that makes interleaved practice superior to blocked practice is the improvement in long-term retention of the skills, given the same amount of training time. This improved retention occurs because interleaved training methods result in enhanced formation of the memory traces involved (Lin et al.). These enhanced neural connections in turn result in improved information consolidation and therefore better long-term retention of the material. This improved trace formation most likely occurs because interleaved training engages more areas of the brain than blocked training (Lin et al. 2008).

It has also been demonstrated that the most effective human learning for practical applications is multi-objective learning rather than simple single-objective learning (Jin and Sendhoff 2006). Blocked practice is usually both single objective and rife with artificial, limiting parameters that limit sensory input and feedback. Blocked training methods also use sterile, artificial contexts that have little in common with the contexts in which operational skill application is required. In contrast, interleaved learning is, by its nature, multi-objective and lacks such rigidly defined, artificial parameters. This not only helps relate the training more directly to practical applications, but it also has been shown to improve neural plasticity, which further enhances information consolidation and long-term retention (Lin et al. 2008).

Improved Operational Performance

The second effect making interleaved practice superior is that it improves operational performance. First, it improves the brain's ability to recall and access information. In general, chaotic network formation in a connectionist learning system results in better chaotic recall performance (Hattori 2009). It is likely that the performance of skills in a chaotic environment assures that the memory trace being utilized for the performance of the skill is the one in the procedural memory system, rather than in the declarative or working (short-term) memory systems. Additional research will be required to verify this prediction.

The second reason that interleaved training improves operational performance is that operational success requires far more than the application of fundamental motor skills. Performing any skill successfully in an operational environment also requires the use of mental processes such as decision-making, contextual evaluation, association, temporal judgment, and stimulus response. Properly designed interleaved training and practice includes the use of these same processes, thereby not only exercising them in the context of operational skill performance, but also linking the centers of the brain responsible for these processes to the neural-networks that are responsible for the performance of the physical skills (Lin et al. 2008). This may also enhance or formulate complex motor learning (Catmur et al. 2008).

Different components of consolidated skills (even within procedural memory) are also retained within different geographical brain regions (Steele and Penhune 2010). Interleaved training methods can be used to activate and link all of the brain regions involved in operational skill performance during the skill training and/or practice period. This allows instructors to use, develop, and link all brain regions that are required for operational performance into patterns of operational performance. These patterns can include decision-making, stimulus response, judgment, contextual association, and motor skill performance, as well as stimulus-related and somatosensory feedback to motor skill performance.[7]

---

[7] Despite its benefits, it is important to note that the chaotic nature and the limited or even nonexistent feedback regarding the performance of highly technical motor skills (such as those required for high-performance gun handling) makes interleaved training methodology less than optimal for developing the initial procedural memory traces that correspond to fundamental motor skill performance for firearms and tactical applications. This is particularly true during complex, scenario-based training or dry-fire training with limited capability for performance-based feedback of fundamentals. Students trained only with this method will perform poorly on fundamental standards evaluations and will have extreme difficulty developing technically correct fundamental skills performance. (See the chapter about our theories of progressive interference versus progressive enhancement for a more detailed explanation.)

The third reason that interleaved learning improves operational performance is because it significantly improves a student's ability to perform learning transfer to contexts and stimuli that may differ from those presented during training. Operational examples could include applying tactical principles to novel environments and formulating new shooting positions or methods of weapon manipulation under duress, based on an injury or to meet a nonstandard engagement requirement.

Research conducted by Mirman and Spivey demonstrated that localization of a neural-network (such as occurs during blocked training) removes the generalization properties of that network, thereby reducing its ability to connect with other neural-networks (2001). As discussed above, interleaved training facilitates the development of not only neural-networks, but patterns of associated neural-networks, which greatly improves the brain's ability to transfer consolidated skills and information across different environments, contexts, and stimuli (Mirman and Spivey 2001). Even simple patterns of neural-networks themselves, while they may comprise more complex motor skills, are not enough for cognition, which requires the development of temporal sequences of patterns (Ans et al.). An example is linking complex skill performance such as dynamic (while-moving) weapons presentation to the judgment and decision-making centers of the brain, relating to the full spectrum of use-of-force-decision-making and dynamic skill performance, including human-based stimulus response and spatial awareness. When compared to simply linking the skill components together, or even simply to a specific stimulus (such as the presence of a firearm), the contrast and benefits are self-evident.

In the most simplistic terms, interleaved training is operationally effective. This is not because it can develop high levels of defined, specific motor skills performance. Rather, it is because it can implant motor skills efficiently into procedural memory and effectively connect the neural patterns required for operational performance within the procedural memory space. For example, it can connect motor skill neural-networks to the associative, cognitive, judgment, and decision-making networks of the brain in such a way so as to facilitate use of these networks while under stress. Fundamental skill performance is certainly not unimportant, but ultimately it is far less important for defining operational success than good and timely decision-making resulting from correct stimulus and contextual associations and responses.

It is critical, particularly for firearms instructors, to note that *interleaved training methods alone will never develop high levels of fundamental skill.* This high skill level may not be important for the three-yard gunfight; however, it is critical for more the advanced tactical applications that *are* sometimes required in most operational environments. Examples include long-distance precision fire and surgical, dynamic close-quarters engagements.

Successful firearms use is in many cases determined by exacting tolerances during the performance of very technically refined motor skills that sometimes also depend on specific equipment. Thus, procedural consolidation of suboptimal technical performance for these skills can effectively act as a governor on a student's long-term performance potential. Therefore, it is important to utilize training methods that are appropriate to the objective of the training session and to design training programs with full cognizance regarding the capabilities, limitations, and long-term operational impacts of the training methods utilized at different stages of a program.

Interference

Not every factor within the purview of instructors and trainers to control contributes to improved consolidation to procedural memory and/or improved operational performance. Some factors prevent these things from occurring or reduce the overall effectiveness of training time and effort. Interference is one such factor.

Interference refers to an effect in which information entering the brain interferes with recall, transfer, or storage of other information. When the information is completely lost, the term used to describe this effect is *catastrophic interference.*

In human beings, interference effects during learning appear to be limited primarily to information contained within the short-term memory system (Shadmehr et al. 1995; French and Ferrara 1999). However, it is also possible that activity which disrupts the primary motor cortex (a significant location of the procedural memory system) may affect or interrupt the transfer and consolidation of information to long-term memory (Richardson et al. 2006).

Particularly for motor skills learning, what happens inside short-term memory appears to be a literal overwrite of the information (Tong et al. 2002). When a new skill requiring use of the same general set of short-term neurons for performance is presented and practiced before a previously taught skill has been consolidated into long-term memory, the ability to perform the first skill and the ability to consolidate it to long-term memory can be lost (Brashers-Krug et al. 1995; Tong et al. 2002; French and Ferrara 1999). Learning one skill and then another in rapid succession (before the first skill has been consolidated and transferred to long-term memory) will result in at least partial loss of the information (Krakauer et al. 2005).

Interference Example—Neural-Based-Learning Results Diagram

Performing a simple motor skill for the first time involves sending electrical signals between the neurons involved (i.e., A–B–C) for that motor skill within the short-term memory system (Figure 1).

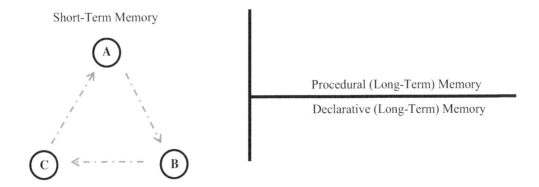

Figure 1

Hebb's Law states that if the neurons fire together repeatedly, they will eventually "wire together" as the connections between them become stronger. The memory then stabilizes, resulting in the formation of a memory trace within the short-term memory system (Figure 2).

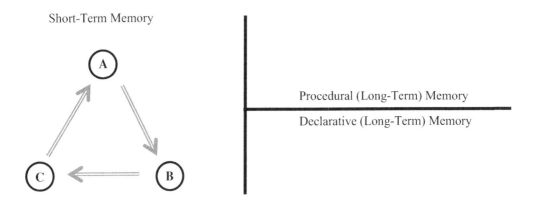

Figure 2

After approximately twenty-four hours, this memory trace in short-term memory is stabilized, then consolidated and transferred into long-term memory. The location(s) in long-term memory may be procedural and/or declarative, depending upon various factors such as the types of training methods used, the type of training environment, and the amount of repetition performed. For most tactical training purposes, the instructor's objective should be to implant the information into procedural memory (Figure 3).

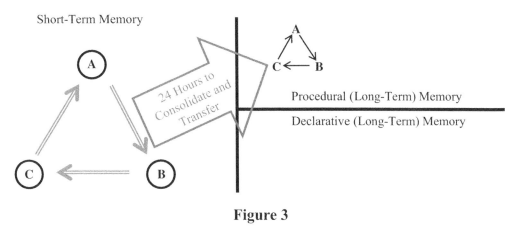

Figure 3

Once the skill has been consolidated into long-term memory, a new skill (D–E–F) that uses overlapping neural space within short-term memory may be learned without interfering with retention of the previous skill (A–B–C) (Figure 4).

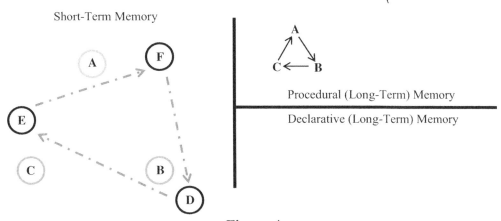

Figure 4

On the other hand, if skill (A–B–C) is taught and then is overwritten (rather than being allowed to consolidate) by skill (D–E–F), followed by skill (G–H–I), the short-term memory space that corresponds to that general type of skill performance becomes cluttered. The clutter interferes with the brain's ability to recognize and transfer the information. This in turn makes it less likely that something correct, if anything at all, will be consolidated/transferred into the long-term memory system (Figure 5).

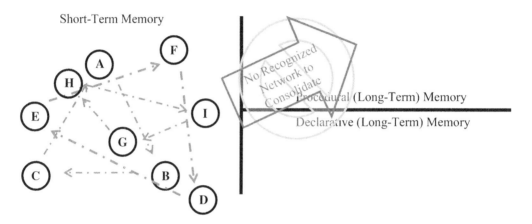

Figure 5

Preventing Interference in Training

The most critical thing that instructional program developers can do to reduce or eliminate interference when training students in tactical skills is to allow students the time necessary to consolidate skills into long-term memory before presenting new, competing skills. Simply, the only way to reliably prevent interference from occurring when teaching similar motor skills that utilize the same short-term memory neural space is to allow at least twenty-four hours from the time that a skill is learned until the time that a new skill is taught (Brashers-Krug et al. 1995; Santini et al. 2001).

A second important aspect for reducing interference is to design instructional programs with continuity of training in mind, particularly as it relates to specific stimuli or situations. Even for information that is consolidated over time, there is evidence that multiple responses to the same stimulus may still cause a type of interference (Caithness et al. 2004). For example, teaching a student to perform two or three different grips on a handgun during weapon presentation will result in the student having difficulty performing any of the grips well during performance under stress—even if all grips are well taught, well practiced, and consolidated effectively into procedural memory. This effect results from a type of "masking" that competing skills have during recall and performance, not from an actual interference in the memory or consolidated skill itself (Criscimagna-Hemminger and Shadmehr 2008).

There is also some evidence that contextual associations may help reduce interference between similar skills (Berthouze and Tijsseling 2006). In other words, potentially competing motor skills may be sorted by contextual association, thereby reducing the competing and interfering properties between the memories.

Declarative Learning

Another somewhat counterintuitive factor that can reduce the effectiveness of procedural consolidation (specifically for motor skills) is combining declarative learning with procedural learning during the same time period (Chang and Gold 2008; Robertson 2009). This effect is specific to waking, off-line consolidation and therefore affects performance of the motor skill itself (Brown and Robertson 2007).

This suggests that the inclusion of extensive declarative learning during tactical motor skills training may actually decrease rather than increase the overall effectiveness of the training time—for instance, teaching great amounts of terminology or tactical concepts along with basic-level motor skills. In general, it may be ineffective to teach students to both do something, and explain or apply it *at the same time*.

It is an important distinction that knowledge within long-term memory (of either system) does not cause these negative effects. Rather, it is the competition between the two memory systems during the learning process. Both types of learning can occur; however, they cannot occur effectively at the same time.

Time of Day

Research suggests that procedural motor skill learning is improved based on the time of day (Della-Maggiore 2005; Grafton et al. 1995). There are likely multiple factors involved. First, the degradation of information and skill performance that occurs when skills are taught in the morning does not appear to occur when skills are taught in the afternoon (Brawn et al. 2010). Second, the combined effects of both the waking and sleep off-line consolidation functions occur during the most optimal time frames related to the instructional period when instruction and/or practice occurs during the afternoon versus the morning (Fischer et al. 2005; Robertson et al. 2005; Santini et al. 2001; Brashers-Krug et al. 1995; Shadmehr et al. 1995).[8]

---

[8] A quick-reference summary of the key information from this chapter is contained in Appendix A.

Chapter 7

Defining a Neural-Network-Based Model
for Training Development

To help design training programs that effectively encode the desired information into the desired memory system(s), by design, we propose a neurologically based modeling tool. This tool is not intended to provide an accurate depiction of neurological processes but rather as a working model of the practical results of those processes. The modeling tool facilitates diagramming individual training sessions, diagramming and tracking student skill development throughout a training program, and structured, neurologically designed development of courses of instruction and training systems. This should be done by working backward from a desired state of skill or knowledge in the intended brain location and then structuring the training program so as to effectively encode the data to those specific areas.

The three brain locations for modeling purposes are short-term memory, long-term procedural memory, and long-term declarative memory (Figure 6).

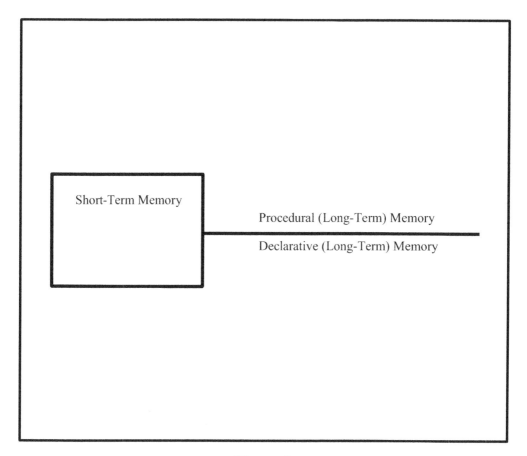

Figure 6

The tool treats short-term memory as a limited-size working space through which we must first pass information in order to code it into long-term memory. Long-term memory is the location where all skills and knowledge must eventually be implanted if they are to be retained and useful. Long-term procedural memory is where all skills, associations, and cognitive processes that may be required under the effects of the sympathetic nervous system must be encoded. Long-term declarative memory is where the knowledge necessary to explain the automatic actions performed by the procedural memory system (for legal and procedural considerations) must be placed.

Because short-term memory space is finite, we define a series of "rules" regarding the types and amount of information and skills that can be placed within short-term memory (Table 2). We acknowledge that further research is required to define the optimal set of rules, and the optimal rules may differ according to demographics such as age, IQ, previous related education or experience, the type of subject matter being taught, gender, specific training techniques, or other factors. The intent of the "rules" is to define a system of parameters that correlates with our observations about general student performance throughout over two decades of both teaching firearms and tactical skills and observing the operational results. This approach enables immediate functional use of the modeling tool while leaving open the possibility for future enhancement as further research is conducted.

The rules are based upon the theory that, within a twenty-four-hour period, properly coded information that is not subject to interference from additional information will be stabilized and transferred in some form to long-term memory for further enhancement (if the information is permanently retained). There are three types of information and six subtypes of information that can be coded. Any additional information beyond the amount allowed during the twenty-four-hour period for each subtype must be drawn in such a manner so as to overlap the previously existing information symbols. These rules apply for both taught and primed information. It is permissible to prime a skill and teach another skill of the same information type (that utilizes the same neural space) during the same twenty-four-hour period.

Able-to-Code Information to Long-Term Memory within Twenty-Four Hours		
Information Type	Information Subtype	Number Allowed
Declarative Knowledge		
	Conceptual	Three
	Rote Memorization	Three
Motor Skill Upper		
	Gross Arm Skill	Two
	Hand/Tool Skill	One
Motor Skill Lower		
	Gross Leg Skill	Two
	Foot Pattern/Skill	One
Visuomotor Skill		One

Table 2

For purposes of this modeling tool, we will define a system of standard symbols. The first symbol is for a physical action, specific motor skill, or piece of knowledge, and it appears as a *triangle. Circles* at each corner represent neurons, and the connecting *lines* represent the connections between them. Because there are several varying stages of a skill's development, there are four distinct symbols utilized within this model to distinguish the various stages of a specific skill's development. These represent priming, training, consolidating, and enhancing. We also have symbols to represent networking or connecting skills together to, for example, build operationally viable sequences such as drawing from the holster.[9]

---

[9]While examples and explanations within this book are specific to firearms/tactical use and the requirement to perform operationally under the effects of the sympathetic nervous system, this modeling tool has tremendous potential to improve training efficiency and effectiveness throughout any industrial, athletic, or educational application.

Skill Symbols

Primed Skill

A primed skill is represented by three "dotted" circles (Figure 7). This represents the presentation of a specific skill (or piece of knowledge) in a scenario where the student is not expected to learn, retain, or fully understand the information presented. The main purpose of priming is to facilitate consistently moving the information through students' "filters" when it is formally taught. The symbol should be labeled with the name of the skill or knowledge primed when appropriate. This symbol can only be present in the short-term memory block.

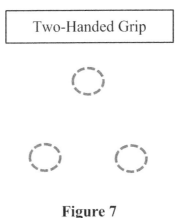

Figure 7

Trained Skill

The symbol for a trained skill (preferably training occurs after the skill has been previously primed in a separate session—to improve the likelihood of consolidation) is a triangle constructed of solid circles connected with dotted lines (Figure 8). This represents a skill in short-term memory *after* it has been trained. For purposes of this model, a trained skill has undergone two of the four stages of development, specifically initial acquisition and stabilization. This symbol can only exist in short-term memory. The symbol should be labeled with the nomenclature of the knowledge or skill involved. It may also optionally be labeled, as shown in Figure 8, with the factors used to contribute to consolidation. These factors should be contained in an arrow pointing to the intended long-term memory space.

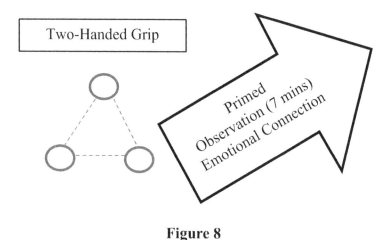

Figure 8

Consolidated Skill

The model's symbol for a consolidated skill is a series of three circles connected by solid lines (Figure 9). This signifies that a skill or piece of knowledge has been consolidated/moved into the long-term memory system. This can be in either the procedural or declarative memory system space.

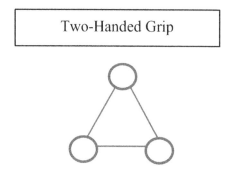

Figure 9

Enhanced Skill

The model's symbol for skill enhancement (during a training session) is the consolidated skill symbol with an extra dotted line on the outside (Figure 10). This represents practice and enhancement during a training session of an existing consolidated skill or piece of knowledge. This symbol can only exist in the long-term memory systems.

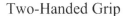

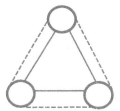

Figure 10

Networking Skills

For the actual operational application of individual skills, it is critical that they be linked with other skills. For example, gripping a handgun must be accompanied by presentation, trigger press, recoil management, and follow-through in order to be applied. This can be thought of as "connecting the dots." When preconsolidated skills are linked together, each individual skill is also enhanced through a process that we call *progressive reinforcement*. It is worth noting that in order to "connect the dots" within procedural memory, there first must be dots to connect.

The model's symbol for connecting (or networking) consolidated skills together is three consolidated skills connected together with dotted lines. This symbol represents developing the connection between existing consolidated skills. These connections probably occur (neurologically) primarily within long-term memory space, as the information being connected exists within long-term memory (Figure 11). The linked skills should be labeled, and the individual skills involved should be notated.

Drawing from the Holster --- Engagement
Grab, Two-Hand Grip, Presentation, Trigger Manipulation, Follow-Through

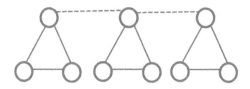

Figure 11

Networked Skills

Once a set of skills has been successfully networked or connected (i.e., the connections between existing skills have been trained and consolidated through a twenty-four-hour period), the symbol used for it is an hourglass shape turned on its side (Figure 12).[10]

Drawing from the Holster

Figure 12

---

[10] Connecting preconsolidated skills into a network is a process that takes place largely inside the long-term memory system. However, even though the skills themselves are already consolidated, the model assumes that connecting the skills in a long-term, retained way still requires time (twenty-four hours) for stabilization and protein synthesis necessary for retention to occur.

Networked Skill Enhancement

Once individual technical skills have been consolidated into a network, plenty of opportunity still exists for those skills to be enhanced and polished (over decades if desired). The symbol for enhancing a skill network is in Figure 13.

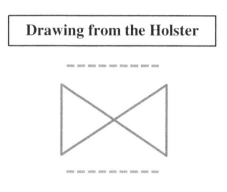

Drawing from the Holster

Figure 13

Other Symbols

Fundamental skill performance (or knowledge acquisition) alone is not sufficient to produce viable operational results. Functional operational application and performance require that skill and knowledge be applied associatively with environmental contexts in response to stimuli and also often after analysis, associations, decision-making, and learning transfer or new skill/concept creation has been performed within the operational environment.

Brain Function

In order to facilitate the planned development of operational proficiency, the connections between these brain functions and the skill performance or knowledge base must intentionally be developed through formalized training. To facilitate accomplishing this, the modeling tool uses a square symbol labeled with the type of brain function (stimulus ID, decision-making, contextual ID, learning transfer/creation, or association and analysis) as well as the specific process being performed. (Figure 14).[11, 12]

Stimulus ID

Hidden Weapon

Figure 14

Linking Skills and Brain Functions

Similar to skills, brain functions can also be linked together (often must be) to build operationally viable results. For example, training police officers to respond to the pure stimulus of a hidden weapon by drawing their sidearms would be extremely poor policy. Many law-abiding citizens in most states carry concealed weapons legally as do many law enforcement officers in plain clothes. Therefore, both contextual associations (i.e., the officer is responding to a domestic disturbance complaint, and makes decisions in accordance with

---

[11] Performance of many of these specific functions will require the previous development (and consolidation) of declarative knowledge. Examples include: signs that a suspect is wearing a hidden weapon, physiological "tells" indicating a potential threat, contextual indicators, departmental use-of-force policy, and so on. For example, in order for a student to react to the stimulus of a hidden weapon, the student must first have the knowledge to identify the hidden weapon.

[12] Engaging multiple brain functions during fundamental skill performance is one of the hallmarks of interleaved training methodology. During fundamental skill development, it is probable that skill performance for any given skill set will be consolidated to both of the long-term memory systems (procedural and declarative). Aside from its other benefits, the engagement of multiple brain functions during skill performance enhancement most likely favors engagement of the applicable neural-networks for the skill that exists within procedural memory space versus those that exist within declarative memory space.

both the law and the department's own policy) should be built into training designed to link presentation of the officer's weapon to this particular stimulus (Figure 15).

This is indicated within the modeling tool by placing the specific skill (or group of skills) at the center and placing symbols for the other brain functions intentionally involved in the training around it in a circle. (We call this arrangement the *skill-performance loop*.) For most tactical applications, this modeling arrangement occurs within the procedural-memory space.

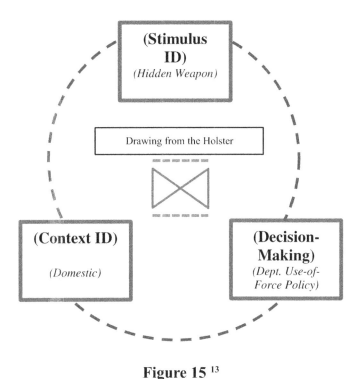

Figure 15 [13]

<hr />

[13] In the model depicted in Figure 15, there is no association/analysis brain function present. While association/analysis would normally be a part of any skill performance loop, the lack of its presence in the modeling diagram may be an indicator of:

1. Specific training-program/training-session design in which this is a known and accepted limitation

2. Specific operational requirement or policy (For example, officers will draw their weapons during all domestic incident responses if a weapon may be present. We are not recommending or endorsing this, it is simply an illustration of the modeling tool's function.)

Layered Skill-Performance Loops

Skill-performance loops may also be implemented in layers within a training session (Figure 16). For example, many operational instances of drawing a weapon from the holster for law enforcement officers do *not* involve engagement of a threat with deadly force.

If we assume that a department's policy mandated that all officers draw their weapons if a concealed weapon is present during a domestic incident response (see above), then training must involve a further stimulus (an accessed weapon) and analysis of that stimulus in accordance with the department policy before deadly force can be applied. In this case (and in most, if not all, real-world applications), the engagement of the threat is actually a separate skill from drawing the handgun from the holster and therefore requires a separate skill performance loop in training. The two may occur simultaneously in some cases, but certainly not in all.

Additional skill-performance loops, including muzzle awareness in 360-degree dynamic environments, communications, and weapons retention would likely be eventually needed within this task (see below) to facilitate full operational competence.

Additional skills may be added inside a specific skill-performance loop. For example, tactically withdrawing from the scene could be a skill added within Loop 1 and other levels of force application (muzzle strikes, Taser, pepper spray, etc.) could be skills added within Loop 2 in the example below.[14]

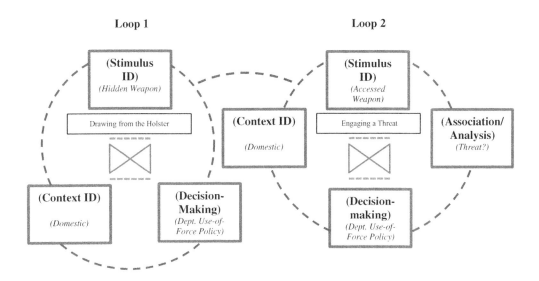

Figure 16

Declarative Knowledge

The symbol for declarative knowledge is a five-pointed star. This indicates information that is intended to be purely declarative in nature (conscious recall only). When either primed or in short-term memory, this star

---

[14] Again, we are neither endorsing nor recommending any type of departmental policy or any operational tactics. This is only for demonstrating the function of the modeling tool.

is dotted (Figure 17). When in long-term declarative memory, this star is solid (Figure 18). The specific subject of the declarative knowledge should be labeled when necessary.[15]

Figure 17

Figure 18

---

[15] The intended purpose of this modeling tool is to provide training developers with a method to identify the type of information and the operationally required brain location of that information. Developers can then apply specific training methodology throughout a complete training program to ensure that the information is coded to the correct part of the brain and linked with the full spectrum of networks required for successful operational performance. In terms of actual neurological function, it is highly probable that most of the information and skills that are retained in long-term memory exist within both the declarative and procedural memory systems. It is also possible that at least some of the procedural memory system's contents are actually transferred there from declarative memory as skills and/or knowledge become more habitual. In applying the modeling tool for training development, the important point is to define the desired operational location of the skill or information and then to use the appropriate training and practice methods to facilitate this outcome.

Task

The task symbol is simply a circle labeled with the specific operational requirement (Figure 19). It is intended as a big-picture, graphical aid to facilitate working backward from the desired operational result to design a training program that will consistently produce the desired results. The task is normally a component of a specific mission area or operational requirement. For example, law enforcement tasks might include use of a handgun, use of a radar detection gun, and interview of a suspect.

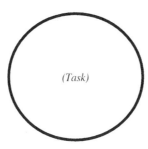

Figure 19

Chapter 8

Theories of Progressive Interference and Progressive Enhancement

One of the unique qualities of the motor skill aspect of firearms training (at least as compared to traditional classroom educational challenges) is the progressive nature of the physical skills involved. We use *progressive* in this context when performance of a specific skill requires the performance of one or more other skills. For example, a sidearm cannot be drawn for an engagement without performance of the distinctly separate (from the act of drawing the weapon) skills of grip, flash sight picture, and trigger manipulation. Thus, the performance of a successful draw (or weapon presentation from the holster) involves not just the performance of the motor skills involved in physically drawing, but also two other distinctly separate motor skills and a visuomotor skill.

Use of the modeling tool facilitates theoretical analysis of the practical neurological effects of various training methodologies at both the micro and macro levels and their probable effects on student retention and operational performance potential. In the following discussion section, we examine a common negative side effect of many common training methods and explore how alternative methodology may not only alleviate this effect but also result in long-term performance enhancements.

Progressive Interference

Most training systems teach skills and information at a pace that is too rapid for the students to learn, transfer to long-term memory, and retain. An ancillary drawback to this initial rapid pace in training is an effect that we call

105

progressive interference. This is when repetitive practice of a skill (such as occurs when performing another skill that involves use of the first skill) is done incorrectly, thereby *reducing* the student's long-term performance potential and overall skill set.

Consider the following example: say a student is taught to perform a single grip, specifically a technically correct combat/modified weaver/isosceles (choose your own terminology here) grip on a semiautomatic pistol (Picture 1).

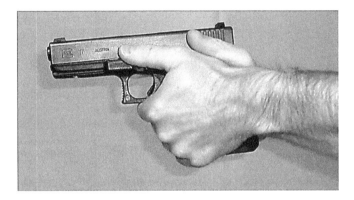

Picture 1

Using the modeling symbolism, let us assume that the neural pattern in short-term memory representing the technically correct performance of this grip is represented by a circuit between three neurons, A, B, and C respectively as shown in Figure 20.

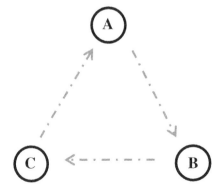

Figure 20: Technically Correct Two-Handed Grip

Assuming that this is the only grip taught to the student, using most standard training models (see the next section for a broader, detailed analysis) this skill will most likely be taught and then repeated by the students during the beginning of the training day. The grip will then be paired with the (separate) skill of trigger manipulation and repetitively practiced again during live-fire practice. Let us assume that, following the live-fire practice, the neural space within the short-term memory system that corresponds to grip on the pistol has been correctly encoded to match what was intended and is therefore accurately represented by the symbol above in Figure 20.

In most courses of instruction, the students will next be taught to present the pistol from the holster. (For simplicity of discussion, let us assume that this is the only other skill taught.) Weapon presentation involves gross-arm-movement skills (differentiated within the model from hand/tool skills). However, for performance of the presentation, these gross-arm movements must be combined with several other distinct hand/tool skills and a visuomotor skill. Specifically, the hand/tool skills include "the grab," pairing the hands, two-handed grip, flash sight picture (a dynamic visuomotor targeting task that is distinctly different from static sight picture—even when performed with both eyes open and target ocular focus), and trigger manipulation. For purposes of this discussion, we will ignore all but the grip.

Let's say that this next progressive skill of presenting from the holster is being taught within the same twenty-four hour period as the grip was taught. This means that although the grip performance has been practiced correctly and stabilization of this skill within short-term memory has begun to occur, the waking downtime (during which the memory cannot be accessed if the information is to be successfully processed) and the sleeping downtime (without which all components of the skill cannot be consolidated and transferred to long-term memory) have not occurred. Recall that *both* of these time periods are a biological requirement for the transfer of this information into either of the long-term memory systems. Therefore, the neural-network that represents the skill performance only exists within short-term memory when the new progressive skill of presentation from the holster is introduced.

Because the "grip" skill only exists in short-term memory, the student cannot perform it unconsciously with technical perfection. Therefore, as new skills using the same short-term neural space are introduced, the conscious processing ability of the student's mind is naturally (and correctly) focused on performing the new progressive skill rather than the previous building block skill. Therefore, significant technical variations in the grip during the progressive skill performance of learning and practicing presentation from the holster are a virtual certainty.

With this concept in mind, we will model the effects of this hypothetical student's progressive skill performance under these conditions. As the student practices his or her presentation from the holster, technically incorrect variations of grip performance will manifest repetitively. Each of them will correspond to a different neural circuit than the correct A–B–C circuit, "cluttering" the neural space within the short-term memory system that corresponds to a technically correct grip (Picture 2 and Figure 21).

Picture 2

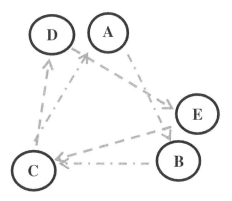

Figure 21

As the training session continues, the student continues to practice the presentation, often while repetitively performing the grip aspect of the progressive skill with a significant level of technical imperfection. With performance and repetition of each new variation of imperfect skill performance, a variation of the original neural circuit is traced within the short-term memory space (Picture 3 and Figure 22; Picture 4 and Figure 23).

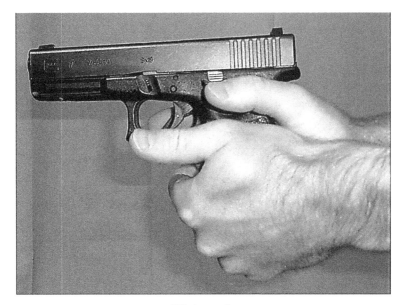

Picture 3

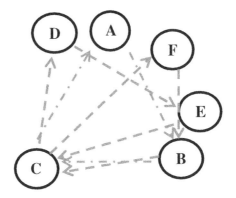

Figure 22

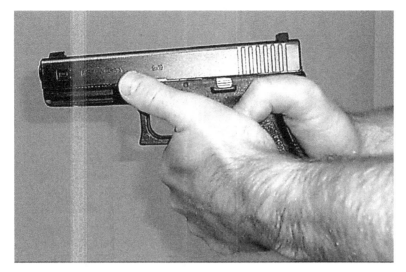

Picture 4

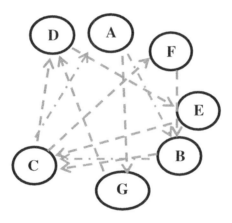

Figure 23

The result, as shown in Figure 23, is a cluttered neural space that contains no recognizable pattern for consolidation and transfer to long-term memory. Therefore, it is impossible to predict what motor skills, if any, the student will develop. This is one of the primary reasons that many experienced armed professionals use different grips virtually every time that they present the weapon, which is in turn a significant limiting factor on operational performance potential. This negative effect of improper instructional design is an example of progressive interference.

Progressive Enhancement

By applying an alternative approach to instruction during the early phases of training, progressive interference can be all but eliminated. Furthermore, the same neurological principles can be used to improve rather than degrade performance as progressive skills are introduced.

Consider the following example: say that a student is taught to perform a single, technically correct, grip on a semiautomatic pistol, as before (Picture 5 and Figure 24).

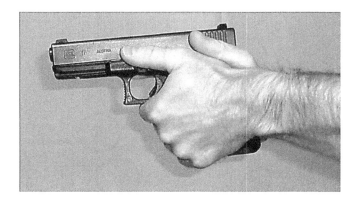

Picture 5

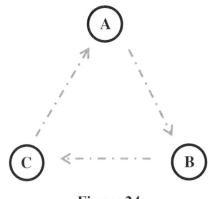

Figure 24

In this case, however, no more information is presented to the student. Instead, he or she is given the appropriate waking and sleep downtime necessary to facilitate consolidation and transfer of this skill into long-term memory (Figure 25).

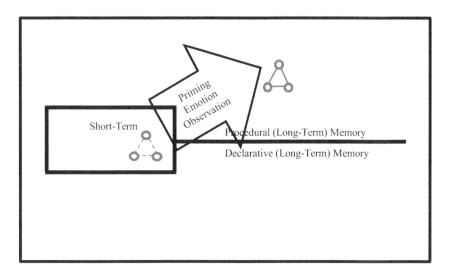

Figure 25

During subsequent training sessions when progressive skills are introduced, the effects are much different from those in the previous scenario. Because the correct performance of the skill has been consolidated into long-term procedural memory, its correct execution during performance of the progressive skill (such as presentation from the holster) can happen unconsciously. Therefore, during the learning process and repetition required to develop a short-term memory trace for the new progressive skill, the existing skill stored within long-term memory can be progressively enhanced (rather than degraded). This occurs through additional, technically correct, performance-enhancing repetitions that are conducted during the learning of the progressive skill (Figure 26). We call this effect *progressive enhancement*.

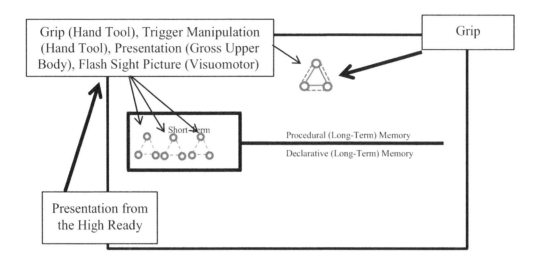

Figure 26

Chapter 9

Defining and Analyzing the Standard Training Paradigm

While there are many variations, the standard model of firearms and related tactical training is generally similar and is based upon blocked methods of instruction. Although this model is the accepted standard, it is inefficient and often results in the creation of significant impediments to performance potential in students. It also produces a limited operational skill set (compared to what is possible) actually being consolidated into procedural memory.

Here we outline the commonly accepted training model from the perspective of its impact on the brain's learning, using the neural-network modeling tool outlined above. We will use the following schedule as a baseline example of the "standard" training paradigm. Then we will apply the modeling tool to examine its effectiveness and efficiency from a neurologically based learning, human-performance-development perspective.

Example Schedule: Standard Training Model, Day One

0730–0830   Introduction and Safety Brief (Classroom)

0830–0930   Fundamentals (Classroom)

                Loading/Function

                Grip/Stance/Sight Picture/Breathing/Trigger

                Manipulation

                Reloading

                Malfunctions

1000–1130   Live-Fire Fundamentals (Range)

1130–1230	Lunch
1230–1300	Multiple Rounds/Recoil Management (Range)
1300–1330	Four-Step Draw (Range)
1345–1430	Multiple Rounds/Multiple Targets
1445–1545	Stress Shooting (Man versus Man)
1600–1730	Fundamental Review and Qualification Shoot

The modeling tool has three sections for data: short-term memory, long-term declarative memory (conscious recall), and long-term procedural (unconscious recall) memory. It requires approximately twenty-four hours, including both waking and sleeping offline consolidation, for information to be transferred from short-term memory to either of the long-term memory systems. Therefore, in modeling of this first day of training, only short-term memory can be used (Figure 27).

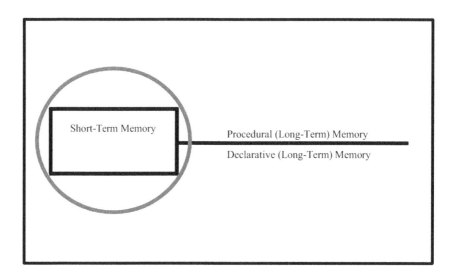

Figure 27: Short-Term Memory

Using only the short-term memory space, we will use the tool to analyze the effects of this hypothetical training day and its effects on long-term memory. The first lesson of the day involves an introduction and the presentation of the standard four fundamental safety rules. Because only three pieces of declarative knowledge are allowed within the model, the fourth rule therefore must overlap within the allowed space. Furthermore, we will assume that a single conceptual piece of learning such as the course purpose from the instructor's perspective is presented during the introductory lesson (Figure 28).

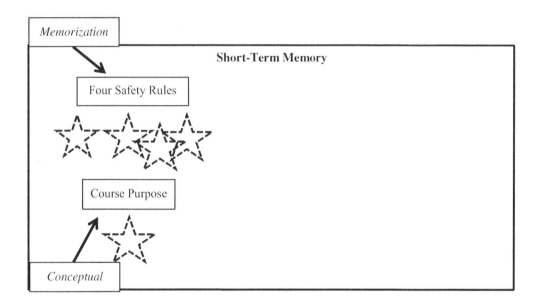

Figure 28: Neurological Map of

Short Term Memory after Introduction and Safety

The next segment of the training day teaches the basic skills necessary in order to conduct a range evolution in a "dry," classroom environment. As defined in the example, the skills taught during this hour-long session include:

- loading/unloading (hand/tool skill)
- grip (hand/tool skill)
- stance (gross-leg skill)
- sight picture (visuomotor skill)
- trigger manipulation (hand/tool skill)
- reloading (hand/tool skill)
- malfunction clearance "hard" (hand/tool skill)
- malfunction clearance "soft" (hand/tool skill)

Using the modeling rules outlined above, the neurological model of the day's training now looks like this (Figure 29).

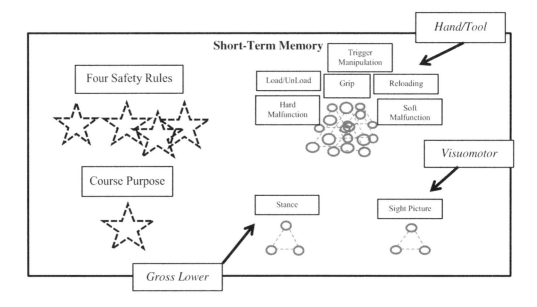

Figure 29: Neurological Map of Training after Classroom Portion

As is now obvious when applying the graphical modeling tool, there is virtually no opportunity for the skills taught in overlapping neural space (hand/tool) to be effectively identified and transferred into the long-term memory system, because there is already no distinguishable pattern for the brain to recognize.

Furthermore, each of the individual hand/tool skills taught contains progressive components that are subject to the effects of progressive interference. Additionally, each component skill may also be performed with a variety of different, technically imperfect methods due to an overload of information presented and an inability of the student to fully comprehend the information and practice each skill—even when consciously focused on it—with technical perfection given the short time period involved. Therefore, each individual neural-network shown above within the hand/tool space can actually be more accurately represented by Figure 30 than by a single, defined network.

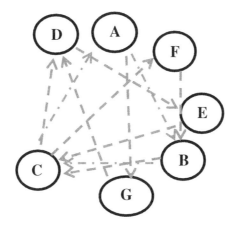

Figure 30: Illustration of Progressive Interference

Thus, the maximum amount of related material that can be effectively taught for a twenty-four period has already been significantly exceeded. The modeling tool demonstrates that the commonly accepted training paradigm significantly exceeds any student's natural daily learning capacity (especially for producing long-term retention) *before* the students are even brought out onto the range.

The negative effects of the standard training model continue as this overload of information is then followed by issuing of live ammunition and skills practice in a live-fire environment (usually within an hour). As noted earlier, often many students are irrationally afraid of the subject matter itself, and most students without significant prior experience (and preexisting skill) have significant fear and stress reactions to the reality of holding a loaded firearm and experiencing recoil for the first time. This fear and stress alters the brain chemistry, affecting consolidation. (Note the lack of a cogent pattern for the brain to consolidate in Figure 29).

If the levels of fear and stress are high enough, it is possible that actions and emotions, particularly those in response to a stimulus (recoil), may become permanently "burned" into the short-term memory space—which makes them very difficult, if not impossible, to unlearn. Again, note the lack of a cogent pattern, and consider the operational result of unpredictable parts of this incoherent mess within short-term memory becoming a more or less permanent fixture that represents the student's performance of these actions or reactions to these stimuli in an operational environment.

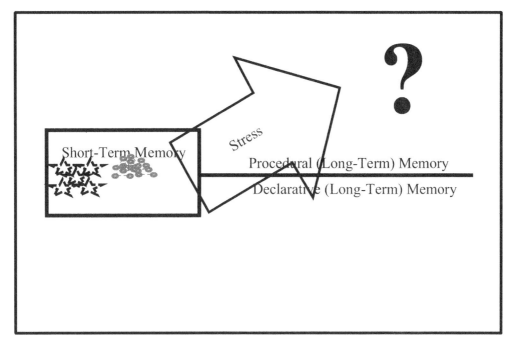

Figure 31: No Defined Patterns Exist for Consolidation and Transfer

After these skills have been trained, additional skills and networked skills are typically added to the program (again within an hour or so of the first skills being presented). These often include presentation from the holster, recoil management/trigger manipulation, and target transitions. Unfortunately, the fundamental skills that need to be "networked" do not yet exist within the long-term memory system. *This means that all attempts at skill linkage must take place within short-term memory only* and can essentially be treated as newly trained skills for modeling purposes. It is also of note that these critical fundamental skills (such as grip and trigger manipulation) and their respective components are cluttered within short-term memory and thus are highly susceptible to interference. They may also be precluded in their ability to be recalled effectively during the conduct of the physiological processes that are involved in the brain's attempt to stabilize the information for eventual transfer to the long-term systems.

By the end of the day's training (consisting of approximately ten billable man-hours per each student and instructor), the state of each student's short-term memory space (assuming they are new students with no prior skill set) can be graphically approximated by Figure 32.

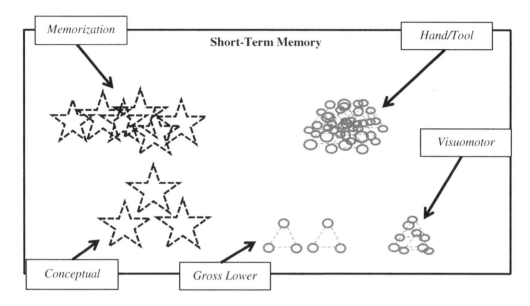

Figure 32: Student Neural Map in Short-Term Memory after One Day of Training

It becomes obvious through the use of the graphical modeling tool that it is impossible to predict with any degree of accuracy what information (if any) will be retained within the short-term memory system by the beginning of the next day's training and/or be transferred to the long-term memory system. Therefore, individual student performance during the next training session will vary widely from student to student, as will the method of technical performance of each individual skill. Furthermore, because there are very few, if any, defined networks that exist in the students' brains following the training session, the long-term retention of information within procedural memory (recall that this makes it accessible during high-stress, critical incidents) is unlikely to occur with any degree of consistency.

By modeling the effects of the neurological processes of learning with a graphical representation of the networks involved, the ineffectiveness and inefficiencies of the standard blocked-training paradigm become clear, as do the negative impacts on the long-term operational performance potential of students trained using this methodology. To increase efficiency and improve both the effectiveness of the training hours and the long-term operational performance results, an entirely new approach to training delivery is required.

Chapter 10

Proposing a New Model of Training Development

Our modeling tool can be applied to help develop more effective and efficient training. It can be utilized in two ways: to review existing training methods for effectiveness of learning and long-term performance potential and to design and develop new, more efficient training programs.

To design a new program utilizing the modeling tool, it is first necessary to outline the requirements that are desired for operational performance. For example, one operational requirement might be self-defense. Once this operational requirement is determined, the essential skill and knowledge components necessary for successful performance of each operational requirement (in terms of brain function) must be identified. When determining these, it is useful to view each operational requirement as a process, rather than an isolated application of knowledge and skill performance. For example, self-defense reasonably can involve a process consisting of threat recognition, mobility, call for help (communication), attempted (active) deterrence, and finally, physical self-defense.

These process steps can then be used to predict, with relative accuracy, the primary tasks that are associated with the operational requirement, each of which can then be subdivided. This step can be completed using a simple table to break down tasks and subtasks, with the knowledge (declarative learning) and environmental considerations (for other training development purposes) associated with each individual task being accounted for and listed. A simple, partial example is shown in Table 3. (This table is for illustrative purposes only; it is not designed as a complete operational blueprint.) New columns can be added for additional subtasks until the all core skills and components of the operational requirement are fully identified.[16, 17]

Once this table is complete, develop the curriculum and design each individual lesson using the modeling tool. Once a specific skill or piece of knowledge has been outlined within the modeling tool (for example, two-handed grip, shooting fundamentals, or presentation from the holster), it need not be fully outlined again but should be marked or annotated to denote that the required subtask is a previously outlined skill (broken down into fundamental components).[18]

---

[16] While this example is focused specifically on teaching physical skills for the sake of brevity and simplicity, the modeling concept can alternatively be used with declarative knowledge also being broken into its fundamental components within the main body of the table. In this case, declarative knowledge and skills could be differentiated by either color coding or labeling.

[17] This application of defining training via tasks and subtasks is unique because the subtasks as defined include not only the progressive physical skill components but also the decision-making, contextual, stimuli-related, environmental, and other considerations involved in the operational application of the skill.

[18] As a general rule, a skill containing the requirement for any other skill as a subtask (i.e., progressive skill development) should not be taught or practiced until the progressive building block skill or skills have been at least primed, taught, consolidated, and enhanced during previous training sessions.

Table 3: Self-Defense Components

Self-Defense

Task	Subtask One	Subtask Two	Subtask Three	Subtask Four	Knowledge	Environment
Identify Threat (Assess)	Recognize Visual Signs of Threat				Contextual ID; Situational Awareness; Hidden Weapon; Weapon ID; Attack Case Study; Attack Recognition	Light; Low light; Driving
	Recognize Audible Signs of a Threat				Threat Verbiage; Situational Awareness	Urban, Rural, Driving
	Recognize Threatening Body Language				Situational Awareness; Read Body Language; Nonverbal Commo; Attack Recognition	Urban; Rural; International
	Recognize Environments That Increase Risk				Threat Indicators; Attach Recognition; Terrain Reading	Urban; Rural; International
Move	Evaluate Environment for Movement Options				Terrain Reading	Urban; Rural
	Decision-Making				OODA Loop; Stress Effects; Process Decisions; Intuitive Decisions; Tactical Decision-Making	Stress; Nonstress
	Conduct Movement	Emergent Movement	Physical Fitness	Running; Crawling; Climbing; Obstacles		Light; Low Light; Summer; Winter; Wet
			Driving			Day Light, Low Light; Summer, Winter, Wet; Ice/Snow; Unimproved Road; Off Road, Urban, Rural

Task	Subtask One	Subtask Two	Subtask Three	Subtask Four	Knowledge	Environment
Call for Help	Verbal					Urban, Rural International
	Phone				Key Phrases	
	Signal				Emergency Dialing	
		Light			Light Maintenance, SOS Code, Light Operation	
		Hands	Hand Signal Performance		Hand-Signals Meaning	
		Improvised			Improvised Signaling Tools, Protective Model	
Deter	Verbal Challenge	Practice Key Phrases			Key Phrases	Urban, Rural International
	Physical Posture	Defensive Posture				
		Hand Position				
		Nonverbal				
	Fight Preparation	Hand Position				
		Barriers		Terrain Nav., Ramming Vehicle, Holding a Line, Ramming Crowd	Terrain-Recognition	Urban, Rural International
		Weapon Access Prep			Decision-Making Law Policy	State, Federal International
		Weapon Access			Decision-Making Law Policy	State, Federal International
		Display			Decision-Making Law Policy	State, Federal International
Physical Self-Defense Skill	Hand to Hand (Unarmed)	Safety	Safety Rules		Safety Rules	Light, Low-Light Summer, Winter Driving, Wet
	Taser					
	Baton					
	Pepper Spray					
	Pistol					

Task	Subtask One	Subtask Two	Subtask Three	Subtask Four	Knowledge	Environment
				Muzzle Awareness		
				Trigger-Finger Awareness		
			Loading			
		Function	Unloading			
			Rounds	Removing Magazine		
			Action	Locking Slide to the Rear		
			Magazine			
			Field Strip			Moving Positional Static
		Fundamentals	Safety	Strong-Hand Component		
			Two-Hand Grip	Support Hand Component		
			Stance			
			Body Position			
			Target-Ocular Focus			
			Sight Picture (Two Eyes)			
			Front Sight Ocular Focus Sight Picture (Two Eyes)			
			Front Sight Ocular Focus Sight Picture (One Eye)			
			Trigger Manipulation			
			Trigger Reset			
			Follow-Through			
			Tactical Follow-Through			
			Recoil Management			
			Assess**			
			Multiple Rounds			
				Assessment**		
				Decision-Making** (Feedback Loop)	OODA Loop / Stress Effects / Process Decisions / Intuitive Decisions / Decisions Tactical / Decision-Making / UoF Law Policy	Stress / Nonstress
				Fundamentals**		
				Follow-Through		

Task	Subtask One	Subtask Two	Subtask Three	Subtask Four	Knowledge	Environment
		Presentation	Decision-Making**			Moving Positional or Static
			Safety**			
			Decision-Making**			
			Extension from High Ready			
				High Ready		
				Decision-Making**		
				Dynamic Grip		
				Flash Sight Picture		
				Dynamic Trigger Manipulation		
				Fundamentals Application **		
			Step Three to High Ready			
				Strong-Hand Grip		
				Hands Meet		
				Vertical Rise to High Ready		
			Holster to Step Three			
				Grab		
				Support-Hand Position		
				Rock from Holster		
				Decision-Making**		
			To Holster			
				Decision-Making**		
				Hand Movement and Positioning		
				Clear Closed Cover		
				Clear Open Cover		
		Clear Soft Malfunction				Moving Positional Static
			Safety**		Soft Malfunction Stimuli	
			Receive Stimulus			
			Finger Off Trigger			
			Support-Hand Tap			
			Magazine			
			Rotate			
			Rack Slide			
			Assess**			
			Fundamentals**			
			Decision-Making**			
	Clear Hard Malfunction					Moving, Positional, Static

Task	Subtask One	Subtask Two	Subtask Three	Subtask Four	Knowledge	Environment
			Safety**			
			Receive Stimulus		Hard Malfunction Stimuli	
			Lock Slide to the Rear (New Technique**)			
			Forcibly Remove Magazine			
			Rack/Clear Chamber and Inspect			
			Reload with Fresh Magazine			
			Rack Slide 3-5x			
			Assess**			
			Fundamentals**			
		Emergency Reload	Decision Making**		Spare Ammunition Location	Moving, Positional or Static Gear Based
			Safety**			
			Receive Stimulus		Empty Weapon Stimuli	
			Drop Magazine			
			Access Fresh Magazine		Location of Ammo	
			Insert			
			Depress Slide Stop			
			Fundamentals**			
			Access**			
		Tactical Reload	Decision-Making**			Moving, Provisional or Static, Gear Based
			Safety**			
			Assess**			
			Decision- Making**			
			Access Magazine		Location of Ammo	
			Release Magazine			
			Catch/Swap Magazine			
			Assess**			
			Decision-Making			
			Assume Modified Two-Hand Grip			
			Stow Magazine		Location for Stowage	
			Fundamentals**			
			Assess**			
		Multiple Targets (Threats)	Decision-Making**			Moving, Positional or Static

131

Task	Subtask One	Subtask Two	Subtask Three	Subtask Four	Knowledge	Environment
					Tactical Considerations for Multiple Threats	
			Safety**			
			Assessment**			
			Decision-Making**			
			Target Transition	Ocular Focus Shift		
				Transition Position (High Ready)**		
				Target Transition		
				Presentation from High Ready**		
				Application of the Fundamentals**		
			Multiple Rounds**			
			Assessment**			
			Fundamentals**			
			Decision-Making**		UoF Decision-Making Law, Policy, Case Studies	
		Retention	Safety**			
			Unarmed Self-Defense Skills**			
			Assessment**			
			Decision-Making**			
			Distance and Terrain Evaluation			
			Movement**			
			Muzzle Strike	Two-Hand Grip**		
				One-Hand Grip**		
				Striking		
				Assessment**		
				Decision-Making**		
			Retention Shooting High Ready	High-Ready Engagement		
			Retention Shooting---Hip	Retention Position		
				Strong-Hand-Only Grip**		
				Support-Hand Position		
				Defense		
				Unarmed Defense Skills**		

Task	Subtask One	Subtask Two	Subtask Three	Subtask Four	Knowledge	Environment
				Assessment**		
				Decision-Making**		
				Extension from Retention Position		
	Rifle	Etc.		Fundamentals**		
	Shotgun	Etc.				

As the example we used to examine the standard training paradigm was entry-level pistol training, we will continue to use it here to demonstrate the use of this process and the modeling tool to develop neurologically effective and efficient training structures. The goal of this process-driven approach to training development is to, *by design*, efficiently and effectively place specific information into specifically targeted areas of the brain.

On the surface, it appears that the essential elements (subtasks) of pistol use are relatively simple (safety, function, fundamentals, presentation, malfunctions, reloading, multiple targets, and retention) and can easily be delivered effectively to students within a one- to two-day period. However, further analysis of additional subtasks, environmental considerations, and required declarative knowledge reveals that full operational performance capability of these seemingly simple tasks is comprised of a surprising plethora of additional subtasks and knowledge. Much of this is progressive in nature, and all of it requires at least twenty-four hours to consolidate to long-term memory *after* it has been successfully coded into the short-term memory system. Therefore, when considering training development, the skill and knowledge first delivered in the course of instruction should be approached from those on the right side of the spreadsheet, beginning with the most fundamental subtasks.

Examination of the table's data shows a pattern with four consistent requirements present regardless of the specific skill involved. Specifically, each skill required for pistol use requires the following subtasks:

1. Safety
2. Fundamentals
3. Assessment
4. Decision-making

Therefore, we can reasonably conclude that these four subtasks (and by default their respective component subtasks and knowledge) are prerequisites that must be appropriately consolidated into long-term memory *before* any of the additional skills are taught. Because safety is a subtask component of the fundamentals (where decision-making is not), it is also reasonable to decide that safety is the first component that should be primed, taught, and consolidated.

Note that some of the essential subtasks, such as assessment and decision-making, are comprised of mental processes and declarative knowledge that are not exclusively associated with pistol use. Therefore, development of these tasks, skills, and knowledge can begin well prior to the introduction of pistol training and is not dependent on pistol/firearms-related training infrastructure or resources. [19]

Safety			
	Safety Rules		Safety Rules
		Muzzle Awareness	
		Trigger- Finger Awareness	
	Loading		
	Unloading		
		Removing Magazine	
		Locking Slide to the Rear	

Table 4: Components of Safety

The essential components of safety as listed in Table 3 are reiterated above in Table 4 for easy reference.

---

[19] Additional research (the results of which may very well end up being site and student-demographic specific) is required to predict with greater accuracy the effects of different training program components on the neurological consolidation of the other components. For example, is it possible to teach a concurrent situational awareness/decision-making skill/knowledge component session and a pistol/firearms skill session within the same twenty-four-hour period without a result of catastrophic interference that severely affects consolidation and retention?

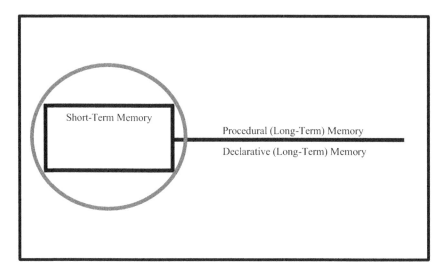

Figure 33: Short-Term Memory Space

The first lesson of the training program (assuming that students are new to the subject matter) will involve only the short-term memory space (Figure 33). The goal is to develop long-term retention, and we already know that priming is one of the most effective methods for achieving consistent procedural consolidation. Therefore, the first presentation of the critical information, especially the physical skills, should be priming only, with no instructor expectation of actual retention (Figure 34).

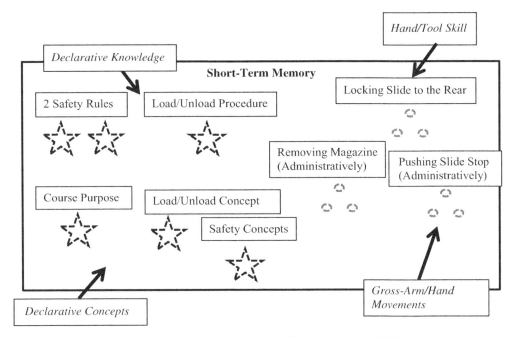

Figure 34: Neural Map of Priming Component of First Lesson

Notice in Figure 34 that the amount of information/skills in each category reaches the limit of what the student can learn/absorb and neurologically consolidate within a twenty-four-hour period (defined by the modeling tool). Recall that information may be consolidated and retained in long-term memory only if all of the information presented is first retained within short-term memory. However, there is no guarantee that all information presented will make it to each student's short-term memory system. Therefore, this first period of instruction is designed as priming only. Retention is neither predicted nor expected.

Compared with the standard training paradigm, this training period contains a relatively small amount of information. This period of instruction, including demonstrations and physical repetition of skills, should take only about forty-five minutes to one hour. The effort expended therefore approximates one man-hour per person. Following this training session, at least twenty-four hours should be provided before any new instruction to allow the full physiological processes of waking and sleep to occur.

The next lesson has two purposes. The first is to teach the skills and knowledge that were primed in the previous lesson (with the primary objective of long-term retention through procedural and declarative consolidation). The second is to prime a new set of skills and knowledge that will be taught during a subsequent period of instruction.

Because the next set of component skills specifically related to firearms/ pistol operation are fundamentals, it is reasonable for this to be the next skill set in the training program. The full content of the fundamentals components (as defined in our example) is reiterated below for easy reference (Table 5).

Fundamentals			Moving, Positional Static
	Safety		
	Two-Hand Grip		
		Strong-Hand Component	
		Support-Hand Component	
	Stance		
	Body Position		
	Target Ocular Focus Sight Picture (Two Eyes)		
	Front Sight Ocular Focus Sight Picture (Two Eyes)		
	Front Sight Ocular Focus Sight Picture (One Eye)		
	Trigger Manipulation		
	Trigger Reset		
	Follow-Through		
	"Tactical Follow-Through"		
	Recoil Management		
	Assess**		
	Multiple Rounds		

Table 5: Fundamentals Components

The first objective of the second training session is teaching the components that were primed within the previous training session. This is graphically represented below in Figure 35. Note that the specific methods used to influence the consolidation of the information are annotated within the arrow showing the intended primary destination memory system. Effective learning involves exhaustive repetition and feedback. The objective is to conduct enough technically correct repetitions under the proper conditions to result in the stabilization, consolidation, and transfer of the information into the desired long-term memory system.

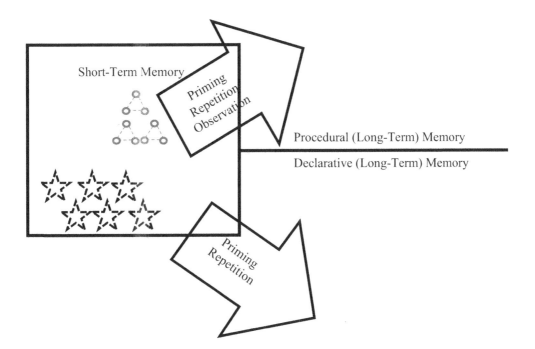

Figure 35: Neural Map of Teaching Effort in Second Lesson

The second objective of this training session is to prime the next set of skills and knowledge, setting the stage for teaching that will occur during the third training session (Figure 36). Recall that there is no expectation or prediction of retention or learning from the priming. Its purpose is to facilitate consistent and effective teaching within a later training session. Therefore, the presentation of information taught during the priming session should be relatively brief. We have found it effective to present priming material about three-quarters of the way through the instructional period and then to finish by reverting back to conducting technically correct review and repetitions of the material that is actually being taught during the period of instruction.

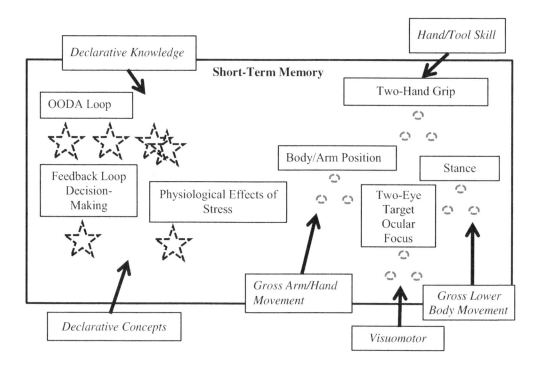

Figure 36: Neural Map of Priming Effort in Second Lesson

This second training period should, again, last approximately one hour. This brings the total man-hours per person expended during the program of instruction to approximately two hours. After the next twenty-four hour consolidation period has elapsed, each student's neural map can be predictably approximated by the diagram in Figure 37. (We have used overlapping symbols to denote that teaching the four components of the OODA loop (observe, orient, decide, act) for memorization exceeds the theoretical model parameters. This may affect long-term retention.) [20]

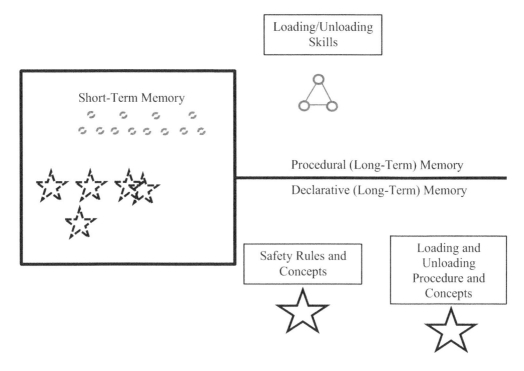

Figure 37: Student Neural Map Twenty-Four hours after Second Lesson

As the number of skills and the amount of knowledge within the respective long-term memory systems increases, so can the length and complexity of the training sessions, if necessary. For all practical purposes within the scope of this model, the long-term memory systems contain an infinite storage space. Furthermore, within our model, enhancement and linkage of networks that exist

---

[20] Note that two-handed grip is labeled as a single hand/tool skill, although it involves separate skills with each of the two hands as labeled in the spreadsheet tool. Recall from the research on observational learning and mirror neurons that each hand appears to possess its own neural space, which facilitates combining two skills (one for each hand) into a single lesson. This approach is supported by our own observations in training, which support the teaching of two-handed grip as if it were a single skill (in terms of neural space considerations) as an effective technique.

141

within long-term memory space occur entirely within this space of infinite size. This means that utilization, enhancement, linkage, or association of information and skills existing within the long-term memory systems can be accomplished *without* encroaching upon the finite short-term memory space, which is limited in size and defined for our purposes by the model parameters.

For example, in Figure 38 we model an example period of instruction that could occur after a significant number of skills and their respective fundamental components have already been consolidated into long-term memory. The period of instruction involves stimulus- and context-based decision-making combined with drawing, engaging on the move, and taking/using cover. These skills may be practiced, enhanced, linked together, and linked with other brain function centers such as decision-making, association/analysis, and stimulus recognition *without* compromising the available capacity of the short-term memory space. This will allow for the teaching and/or priming of new information and skills (in this case, priming some low-light and flashlight skills) during the same period of instruction or twenty-four hour period of training.

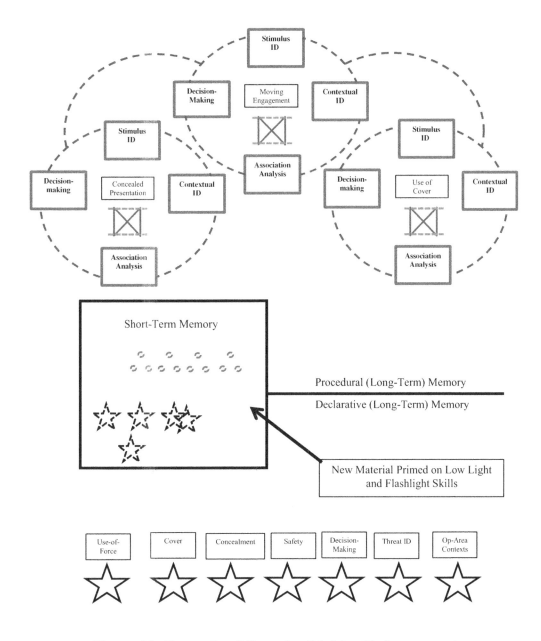

Figure 38: Example of Complex Linking/Enhancement
Combined with Simple Priming

As demonstrated above, our recommended training principles along with the modeling tool can facilitate the design of training programs that target information efficiently and effectively into specific areas of the brain. These can also help us predict, design, and develop the neurological processes within our students' brains that are required for optimal operational success. The spreadsheet facilitates tracking and comparing the development of students' neural-networks to the predesigned network models required for operational performance. The graphical modeling tools facilitate easier analysis and understanding of the effects of lesson design and instructional techniques on the students' capacities to absorb, retain, and ultimately apply the information being taught.[21]

---

[21] ISS has developed an integrated spreadsheet/graphical modeling tool. Both its use and the full extent of applying this research and methodology are outside the scope of this book. For more information on our instructional design, integrated skill development, and integrated skill enhancement systems, please contact us at www.i-s-solutions.com.

Chapter 11

Addressing the Problem: Recommendations for Applying Research to Tactical Training System Design and Delivery

At the beginning of this book, we discussed a number of the challenges faced by the training industry and defined the makeup of the training industry using the context of a four-sided "box." The structure and capabilities of this box are defined by the four primary forces that impact the training industry: vendors, competitive shooters, elite units, and liability. At the same time, the limitations inherent to each of these factors act not only as limitations on the industry itself but also as limiting factors on the operational potential of the students we train.

Our intent here has been to combine our own unique experiences in both training and operations with the latest in applicable scientific research, addressing how and why people perform effectively in operational environments as well as how we, as trainers, can most effectively and efficiently prepare our students for success in the field.

Whenever challenges or deficiencies in a training program or in an organization's operational performance are recognized, an almost instantaneous standard reaction is to blame the shortcomings on a lack of resources. This is usually followed by an attempt to address the problem by "throwing money" at it.

It is true that resource limitations are (and will always be) a significant challenge for most professional trainers. It is equally true that new resources, funding, equipment, and training time have the potential to improve the results of virtually any training program. However, we challenge the notion that

145

throwing additional resources into the "box" of the existing training paradigm can adequately address many common training shortfalls or the operational mishaps that can result from them.

Instead, we submit that fundamentally restructuring how we train by applying the latest principles indicated by neuroscience research can give us the answers to today's (and tomorrow's) challenges. As an added benefit, restructuring and reprioritizing the fundamental approach to the training using these principles will result in significantly improved efficiency in the ratio of resource expenditure to operational performance potential. In other words, applying this research will limit our dependence upon resources as a solution and even has the potential to facilitate an overall *reduction* in training budgets to accompany improvements in performance. With this in mind, we present the following recommendations:

1. Redefine the objective.

Virtually all training within the current tactical paradigm (particularly firearms) is based around an outcome-based model of performance standards. In fact, an oft-heard, sometimes proudly uttered sentence from tactical trainers is "We train to standard, not to time." Effectively, this means that the hours spent training are not considered important; only the achievement of the standards is. Therefore, why waste time training if the standards have already been achieved? (In fairness to many of these trainers, if their instructional systems and available tools are designed only to produce achievement of the standard, students who already meet it may not benefit from further instruction using those systems and tools.)

In this book, we have presented and supported our hypothesis that an alternative approach will improve firearms and tactical training. Specifically, the objective of a tactical training system should be to code, connect, and enhance the full spectrum of neural-networks that account for desired operational performance into students' *long-term* memory systems. The specific system (procedural or declarative) depends on the operationally required use of the skills and information. However, for the purposes of critical incident performance, the information must be coded into procedural memory.

Tactical training systems design should be restructured from outcome-based performance evaluation to targeted neural-network development and enhancement.

2. Design and utilize standards appropriately.

It is important to clarify that we do not suggest the elimination of standards within tactical training programs. The primary reason for them is straightforward and can be effectively summarized in a single word: liability. Very simply, there must be something concrete, quantifiable, and documentable that justifies an administrator qualifying an armed professional and placing him or her on duty in the field.

This requirement for an empirical, documented standard of qualification is important and will never go away. However, we submit that structuring training programs (particularly with firearms) in an outcome-based manner that is *focused* on meeting these qualification standards is a suboptimal approach.

The reasons for this are simple. First, standards are not indicative of operational application of the skills, nor can they ever be. The broad array of challenges and large quantity of unknown variables that are inherent to critical incidents preclude this possibility. Second, standards can be met in a sterile testing environment, using information and skills that are stored only in the short-term and/or long-term declarative memory systems. Although meeting standards based on skills and information within these memory systems meets liability and paperwork requirements, it does little to prepare students for operational performance. As we have demonstrated, information in these memory systems may be overwritten or inaccessible during actual operational performance in the field, particularly under the physiological effects of the stress response.

Let there be no doubt; standards are indispensable. They are critical for liability and administrative purposes. They can also be used as a highly valuable feedback mechanism for instructors, program developers, and administrators. In fact, standards can and should be used to facilitate well-informed quality assurance, quality control, and continuous improvement processes. However, standards should be acknowledged for what they are and should not be utilized as the *objective* of training.

Standards are tools for liability control, administrative control, and training system feedback; they should neither be viewed nor utilized as a training objective.

3. Restructure training systems.

Our theory is that existing tactical training systems largely ignore the limitations inherent to the short-term memory system and the biological processes required to assure long-term storage of skills and information. As a result, a significant amount of the training time dedicated to developing tactical skill sets within the current training paradigm is unproductive, and a strong argument can be made that much of it is actually counterproductive. In any case, there is little doubt that tactical training structures in common use are both highly inefficient and minimally effective relative to the amount of resources expended.

Training systems should be fundamentally restructured based on how the human brain learns and retains skills and information.

With this in mind, we make the following specific recommendations regarding the restructuring of tactical training systems:

a. Prioritize effectiveness in learning before efficiency in delivery.

Far too much emphasis is currently placed on *efficiently presenting* information and skills at the beginning of training programs. While the information is presented, very little of it is actually retained, while what is retained is highly inconsistent from student to student and is largely unpredictable. This ultimately both severely limits operational performance potential and wastes significant portions of limited and valuable training time. Most trainers will acknowledge that they dedicate the majority of their time, even in a multiweek instructional program, attempting to bring many of their students to minimal performance levels on what is presented in the first few hours of the program.

Training systems should be designed so that the students *effectively learn* all of the information as it is presented.

b. Control the quantity of information based on the limitations of short-term memory.

One of the primary shortfalls in current training methods is that too much information and too many skills are presented in too short a time. When this occurs, information in general suffers from the effects of interference, and many technical motor skills are affected by progressive interference as defined previously in this book. These problems negatively affect operational performance potential and waste valuable training time.

Specific periods of instruction should be designed to only present the amount of information that can be coded into the short-term memory system.

c. Provide both waking and sleep off-line time within twelve hours of training periods.

We have documented that long-term retention of skills and information is the result of a series of biological processes in brain, including the transfer of information from the short-term memory system to a different geographical location within the brain, where it must be recoded. Research indicates that some of the processes necessary for this can only happen when the information is not being accessed or used while awake; others can only happen during sleep. In order for the full spectrum of processes necessary to transfer and consolidate skills and information to long-term memory to occur, both of these periods (sleep and waking off-line time) should occur within twelve hours of the training period.

Following training periods, both waking and sleep off-line time should be provided to the students within twelve hours.

d. Separate instructional periods by at least twenty-four hours.

We have documented that after information is coded to short-term memory, it is susceptible to interference (being overwritten or corrupted) for twenty-four hours. If new skills or information that use the same neural space are presented within this time frame, both sets of skills or information are highly susceptible to disruption, thereby affecting long term-retention and operational performance potential.

There should be at least twenty-four hours separating instructional periods that will cover new skills and/or information that utilize the same neural space within short-term memory.

e. Apply the instructor-controllable factors influencing consolidation to code and enhance targeted neural-networks within specific areas of the brain.

We have presented our hypothesis that the full spectrum of components and information necessary for operational performance under stress must be consolidated to the procedural memory system. In this book, we have identified twelve instructor-controllable factors that can both help and hinder this process. They can also be used to enhance information already stored in this memory system. Similarly, there are likely components of any tactical training system (for example, the detailed knowledge to provide a legally viable explanation of one's actions after an incident) that should be targeted to declarative memory.

It is unlikely that all of these factors will be applicable within any single training session. However, this methodology should be used in an informed and intentional way. This will improve both long-term retention and operational performance.

Periods of instruction should make intentional, informed use of the instructor-controllable factors that influence procedural consolidation.

4. Exploit interleaved training methods to link and enhance skills within procedural memory.

We have previously presented research suggesting that interleaved training is one of the most powerful yet under utilized tools available to trainers. It not only favors skill enhancement within procedural memory, but it also links the multiple brain functions required for operational performance within procedural memory. Therefore, after the initial memory traces for the required skills and information have been consolidated to long-term memory, we submit that increasingly complex interleaved training should quickly become the primary training method and should consume the bulk of the remaining available training time.[22]

After skills and information have been consolidated to long-term memory, the majority of the available training time should be focused on applying interleaved training methodology.[23]

---

[22] Applying interleaved training methods will, in most cases, preclude the use of live-fire training techniques. After all, human interface and human-stimulus-based decision-making are two of the most critical components of virtually all operational applications of firearms and tactical skill sets. Only in extraordinary training circumstances for highly skilled personnel within the most elite, specialized units (if even then) can a legitimate argument be made for placing live role-players in front of the muzzles of loaded weapons. Therefore, engaging the full spectrum of brain functions and skills required for operational performance will necessarily involve the utilization of a preponderance of non-live-fire training techniques.

[23] A summary of these recommendations is contained in Appendix B.

Chapter 12

Training Issues and Safety

Considering our recommendations above, particularly regarding the application of interleaved training, we feel it is important to discuss some of the potentially controversial issues these recommendations raise.

Live Fire versus Dry Fire

The notion that firearms training can (and should) be conducted predominantly without the use of live ammunition is a concept that has become increasingly mainstream in recent years. There are also many excellent, highly experienced instructors and operators who would challenge this idea, and they are right to do so. It is a fact that the method of "shooting until you get better" works, and many of its proponents have the operational experience, the competitive success, or both, to prove it.

Note that we do *not* advocate training students who will carry firearms for a living (or for self-defense in the civilian sector) without the use of live fire. Some recent peer-reviewed research suggests both that this possible and that it can produce technically better shooters than live-fire training (Kratzig 2014; Kratzig and Hudy 2011; Kratzig et al. 2011). However, we believe that it is noteworthy that these studies were based entirely on an outcome-based model utilizing administratively designed qualification standards focused largely around traditional marksmanship skills. As a result (in our opinion), the quality of the specific standards used corrupts the data set for operational purposes. However, operationally applicable or not, these studies do corroborate our experiences and research, both of which suggest that less live-fire and smarter

153

training methodology can not only improve efficiency but can also enhance both student operational performance and long-term skill retention.

We believe that, instead of focusing around whether training should be conducted with live-fire or dry-fire techniques, training developers and instructors should focus on what they are teaching, its relevance for the students' specific operational needs, and how they can most effectively code or enhance it in the desired long-term memory system. In some cases, this will require live fire. In many cases however, it will not. If coding or enhancing the skill(s) in long-term procedural memory does not *require* live fire (which is expensive, time-consuming, resource intensive, and always carries the risk of serious injury or death) then why should it be used, particularly if time and resources are limited?

In many cases, skills can be coded, consolidated, enhanced, and networked very effectively, and often even more effectively, *without* the use of live-fire training methods. In other cases, live fire is the only method that can effectively produce or enhance the desired neural-networks. By using training development techniques such as our proposed modeling tool, these skills and objectives can be differentiated and training can be designed to capitalize optimally on the use of time, facilities, and resources while developing the neural-networks necessary for operational success within the appropriate memory systems.

The "shoot more rounds until you get better" method is like using a misting sprinkler to fill up a water glass from ten yards away. It *will* fill the glass, given enough water and time; however, it is certainly not an optimal use of either resource. In contrast, training methodology that specifically develops and enhances the applicable neural-networks, targeted to specific memory systems by design, can be thought of as filling a water glass directly from the tap, thus saving significant amounts of both time and water.

In summary, we agree that a student cannot effectively learn operational shooting skills without live ammunition any more than a water glass can be filled without water. However, we submit that appropriately designed and delivered training systems can significantly reduce both the time and the amount of ammunition required to produce high quality operational performance.

Ten Thousand Decisions

It is intriguing that one of the standard benchmarks for the quality of a tactical training program and its resulting operational skill is often the amount of ammunition expended per trainee. The Federal Bureau of Investigation, widely considered the leading law enforcement organization in the world, once had an informal mantra associated with its academy firearms training program: "Ten thousand rounds per man." In fact, the liability considerations associated with this standard assumption result in an often-voiced (justifiably) administrative objection to reducing round counts in organizational firearms and tactical training programs. What administrator wants to accept responsibility for voluntarily *reducing* the round count associated with a tactical training program?

In light of our training experiences and research, we challenge the assumption that associates the number of rounds fired with training quality. Instead, we propose an alternate mantra for any training program that is intended to produce operational tactical competence: "Ten thousand *decisions* per man."

Reviews of both law enforcement and civilian use of deadly force show that the need for extremely high levels of fundamental technical skill (as compared to competitive shooting or special-missions-unit requirements) is extraordinarily rare, so rare as to be statistically insignificant. In contrast, even a cursory glance at today's news headlines shows that extremely high levels of associative judgment and decision-making skill are of the utmost importance, no matter the job title or relative skill level of an armed professional (or civilian).

If we accept that expert-level decision-making skills are more important to both operational success and organizational liability mitigation than expert-level technical shooting skills, then it follows that the ultimate quality of a tactical training program should not be directly associated with the number of live rounds fired. Instead, it should be judged by the amount of times that the *human-stimulus-based* recognition and decision-making neural-networks are linked (successfully) with the neural-networks representing the performance of the physical skills for applying the varying levels of the force continuum.

Are Cooper's Rules Obsolete?

Colonel Jeff Cooper was the founder of Gunsite Academy and is widely considered the father of modern weapons craft. Certainly, by any measure, he was one of the most influential industry figures of the last century, contributing a legacy of game-changing ideas, including the color-coded levels of situational awareness for combat mindset and the four fundamentals of firearms safety. These safety rules in particular are still widely recognized as *the* standard for all firearms-based operations and include the concepts of always treating all firearms as if they are loaded and never pointing *any* firearms at a person unless that person presents an actual threat.

There is a very good reason that Cooper's safety rules have become universally adopted across the industry. Simply, they work. If you follow them religiously, you can't have firearms accidents in training, period. However, there is a flip side to the coin. If firearms skills (including use-of-force judgment and decision-making) aren't performed in response to human stimuli with great frequency in accordance with the principles of neurological network development, *the most important aspect of the operational skill set cannot be developed*. We submit that it is worth considering a reevaluation of dogmatic adherence to Cooper's principles of firearms safety in organized tactical training programs.

Let's begin with Cooper's first rule: all guns are always loaded. On the practical, safety side, the beautiful simplicity of this is obvious. It is true; very rarely do firearms accidents involve "loaded" guns. One simply does not pick up a loaded gun and point it at a friend, family member, pet, or valued piece of personal property. Most of these avoidable tragedies occur when the people involved (often both parties) are unaware of the actual condition of the weapon at the time of the event. Cooper's rule precludes this. Always act as if it is loaded, and you will never make a mistake.

In actuality though, firearms are *not* always loaded, and the letter of this rule is frequently violated by every person who handles a firearm. Even the simple process of cleaning, reassembling, and performing a function check on a weapon necessitates fundamental violation of this rule. The fact is that guns are only loaded when there is ammunition in them and, when it is absent, they are little more than expensive hunks of metal and wood or plastic, presenting little danger to anyone as anything more than a club. In point of fact, there is nothing fundamentally unsafe about an unloaded firearm. The danger lies in uncertainty about a weapon's condition at any given time and in failing to build associative habits that eliminate or at least greatly reduce the possibility of tragic accidents.

We feel that there are some potential issues with this first rule that manifest with negative effects regarding weapons safety during both training and operations. The first is that in some ways, this rule sets an expectation of oblivious incompetence for firearms users, implying that they cannot be expected to (and ultimately will not) be cognizant of the condition of the firearms they handle nor competent enough to check them. We submit that setting this expectation is different than designing procedures for both training and operations that take into account that people will make mistakes and equipment will malfunction.

The second potential issue with this rule is that it is fundamentally based on an untruth, which taints the credibility of the system itself. Furthermore, the rule itself must be frequently ignored by virtually all who handle firearms for purposes beyond that of a range familiarization during situations that include cleaning, assembly, and disassembly. In essence, it is the universal rule that always applies—except when it doesn't. Stated humorously, "It works sixty percent of the time…every time." We suggest that this rule, while certainly effective for range operations, in fact contains some fundamental flaws that may contribute to the large percentage of negligent discharges that occur during administrative weapons handling such as loading, unloading, cleaning, and maintenance.

Cooper's second rule can be summarized by stating that the muzzle of a weapon should never cover anything that the user is not willing to kill or destroy. This is excellent advice and works very well on a firing range. Off the range, particularly in an urban environment, it is almost impossible to use a firearm (even if it is not fired) without at some point violating this rule. Where, for example, inside a multilevel apartment building, could a muzzle be pointed that does not violate this principle? Furthermore, both law enforcement and civilians who use firearms for self-defense point weapons in directions and at people that they hope *not* to kill or destroy (although tactically they should normally be willing to do so), and they do it all the time with great effectiveness toward deterring the need for actual application of deadly force.

We submit that, rather than constructing a range-based safety infrastructure that does not adequately translate into the operational environment, it is ultimately more beneficial to use an infrastructure that works in all environments and to build the skill necessary to facilitate its effective use. Rather than focusing on where firearms should *not* be pointed, often leaving the practitioner on the street with no viable alternatives that fall within the accepted safety paradigm, we propose focusing the safety infrastructure on where firearms *should* in fact be pointed at any given time—and why.

In the profession of arms, it is a fact that firearms are carried and used for only one purpose: to point them at people. Without a person on the other end, there is no need for the use of a firearm. Therefore, a fundamental structure that precludes this from occurring in training, regardless of the actual condition of the weapon, is extremely limiting with respect to developing operational performance potential. This is particularly true with regard to human-stimulus recognition and the associated decision-making and motor-skill responses that correspond to the appropriate use-of-force. In essence, this second rule for training safety in many ways precludes effective preparation for operational safety.

There is growing recognition of this problem, and over the past several decades, focus has increased on force-on-force decision-making and simulator-based decision-making training, particularly for military and law enforcement personnel. These are both excellent training tools; however, they are limited in their effectiveness, mainly because they are expensive and resource intensive, requiring specialized equipment and facilities. Trainers also have difficulty providing the repetition necessary to build and enhance the required neural-networks within procedural memory when using these tools. In contrast, placing a role-player "downrange" during the organized performance of dry-fire skills can provide the opportunity for almost unlimited repetitions in stimulus recognition, decision-making, and appropriate motor skill response. This can be done in a dry-fire environment far more progressively and for a fraction of the cost of simulators or force-on-force tools, without the need for any specialized equipment or facilities.

We are certain that most trainers will (understandably) balk at the concept of putting role-players in front of the muzzles of live weapons (even unloaded ones), so we will discuss this concept further.

Aside from quoting Cooper's rules, the primary argument against this type of training methodology, particularly for law enforcement personnel, is the claim that police officers simply cannot be trusted to ensure that their weapons are unloaded. This is a valid concern. The bullet holes in the tables and walls of virtually every weapons cleaning room at virtually every police department speak to its legitimacy. We submit that, while this concern is valid, the fact that it is valid should itself give us some pause. If police officers in the aggregate are not capable of ensuring that their weapons are unloaded within the context of a formal, structured training evolution, then why should they be qualified to carry and use firearms professionally and make deadly force decisions in service to the general public? We suggest that this concern, while legitimate, is a symptom resulting from failures inherent within the existing training paradigm rather than an indicator that training methodology incorporating interleaved dry-fire is fundamentally unsound.

Ignoring use-of-force considerations for a moment and looking at it purely from an operational safety perspective, one of the biggest limitations of the traditional, live-fire-based, Cooper-structured paradigm is that its structure precludes allowing the possibility of student safety failure in training. It is (and must be) the first priority of a firearms trainer to ensure the safety of students. No legitimate instructor will allow the possibility of failure when it comes to the potential for students or role-players to end up facing the business end of a loaded firearm due to a student's failure to correctly perform a challenging exercise that pushes and develops his or her capability in this area. With the exception of perhaps some special-missions-unit activities, which are far beyond the scope of most training requirements, any instructor who does so is, in our opinion, negligent.

Nevertheless, almost every "real world" application of a firearm is likely to involve multiple moving "no shoots," at least one moving target, a moving shooter (ideally), and a dynamic backdrop and landscape behind and/ or in front of the intended target. The fact is that the dynamics of the likely environment, even for a civilian self-defense firearms application, *cannot* adequately be simulated or prepared for in a live-fire setting. Furthermore, we submit that Cooper's rules fall somewhat short in this regard, both as they relate to limiting training and providing real, viable alternatives during operations that fall within the scope of the defined safety infrastructure.

For the learning of complex tasks to take place, the capability for failure to occur during the learning process is critical. Without the ability to fail, mistakes cannot be made, feedback cannot occur, and therefore learning and enhancement are both precluded. When trainers construct training environments in which safety failure is a nonoption, the ultimate harm manifests in operational environments that are made less safe for the shooter, any teammates, and the general public. This reduction in operational safety occurs through a lack of preparedness for addressing the many complex and potentially deadly challenges such as muzzle position and mobility in dynamic environments. These cannot be adequately addressed by Cooper's rule book or prepared for in a live-fire environment where failure at risk of life or limb is not acceptable. In contrast, properly constructed, sterile (of live ammunition), dry-fire environments are ideal for addressing these training challenges. They also require very little in the way of additional resources and are, in some ways, both safer for the students and more effective for training than even simulator and force-on-force tools can be. In these dry-fire environments, students can be progressively trained with increasingly complex and challenging interleaved methodology, effectively and consistently building a robust, operationally functional skill set that simply cannot be produced efficiently through any other currently known training techniques.

Cooper's model for firearms safety and the traditional, live-fire-based training model both include inherent limitations. Specifically, the safety model limits training potential. It also fails to encompass the full scope of modern operational requirements, while the zero tolerance for failure in critical safety areas that is required in live-fire environments precludes efficient higher-level learning and complex skill enhancement in these areas. These limitations are particularly harmful with regard to their ultimate effects on *operational* safety and the ability to efficiently and effectively develop a comprehensive operational skill set in students. Skills affected include but are not limited to muzzle control in dynamic 360-degree environments and appropriate regulation of the application of deadly force in response to dynamic, human-based stimuli in rapidly changing environments. Therefore, for developing modern training systems, we propose that certain aspects of both the live-fire-based training paradigm and Cooper's traditional safety infrastructure may not be well suited to produce optimal operational results.

Alternative Firearms Safety Structure

It would be both unfair and of minimal use to question the modern applicability of Cooper's safety model without providing an alternative. Therefore, we will attempt to do so. In the context of this firearms safety structure, a *rule* is defined as something that always applies in all environments and should never be broken, whether dry firing, cleaning, plinking tin cans, or shooting it out in a running urban gun battle in a combat environment. A *recommendation* is something that should be trained as a habit but may not apply in all situations and environments.

Within our proposed safety structure, there are two rules accompanied by three recommendations.

Firearms Safety Rules

1. Always know where the muzzle is pointed; point it there intentionally.

2. Never place a finger on the trigger unless intending (or willing) to press it.

Firearms Safety Recommendations

1. Check the condition of a weapon each and every time it is handled.

2. Do not place a finger on the trigger unless the sights are aligned on a target.

3. Be sure of the target and what is in front of and beyond it.

The meaning of the *rules* is clear. Muzzle and trigger-finger awareness are key. If the muzzle and the trigger finger are both appropriately controlled, there will be no accidents resulting from human error. Note that these rules do not preclude or ignore the real possibility that there may in fact be no "safe" place to point a weapon in an operational environment. Instead, they recognize that such a place may not exist and construct the safety paradigm around developing the user's situational awareness and *informed intent* with respect to weapon-handling decisions. This is backed up by the ultimate factor in firearms safety: control of the trigger finger.

The *recommendations* are all practices that should be trained into habit, yet may not apply in all operational applications. For example, while a user should "always" check the condition of a weapon upon touching it, when actually drawing a weapon in self-defense, he or she will not and should not stop to verify whether a round is in the chamber. Likewise, while always being sure of the target and the surrounding environment is a critical operational skill, strict adherence to this as an inviolable "rule" precludes the application of area fire, defilade fire, and some applications of suppressive fire. While these techniques may not apply in many environments or for most operational requirements, it defeats the purpose of a "safety rule" within our definition if there are times when it must be ignored. Finally, with respect to associating sight picture with trigger-finger position, this is something that we believe should be intentionally trained into procedural motor memory. However, there are applications, specifically including close-contact situations, where a traditional "sight picture" will not be utilized when pressing the trigger. Because there are exceptions, we do not define this recommendation as a rule.

Interleaved Training Method Tool Alternatives

We have demonstrated the viability of interleaved training methodology as the primary training method once consolidation of the basic motor skills is complete. We have further argued that using a dry-fire environment, including live role-players, is currently the most resource-efficient and effective way to conduct this training. However, we acknowledge that while effective and efficient, this is neither free from risk nor appropriate for every organization or training environment. Therefore, we provide a brief, comparative overview of not only the live-weapon option but also several alternatives that can potentially be used to achieve similar results. Please note that the following discussion is neither intended to be all-inclusive nor fully comprehensive in its scope.

Live Weapons

Utilizing "live" (defined for this discussion as fully functional) weapons to conduct dry-fire training, up to and including interleaved training with role-players, offers a number of distinct advantages. The first, and most obvious, is the cost savings that it brings. An organization that must train its personnel to use weapons, by definition, already has live weapons. Specific drills and training techniques are beyond the scope of this book, but an organization that possesses weapons and magazines (assuming semiautomatics) already has everything it *needs* to build and enhance very high levels of operational capability.

There is another significant advantage as well, particularly in a law enforcement setting. That is that using an officer's actual duty weapon during frequent dry-fire training evolutions helps ensure that it remains functionally clean. Routine manipulation and functioning helps to clear gathering dust, corrosion, and lint that can cause operational malfunctions in rarely manipulated weapons. Use of the duty weapon also familiarizes the officer with the specific, unique characteristics of his or her individual weapon, including trigger press and any individual modifications that may be allowed by organizational policy. This is particularly valuable if officers are provided an individual choice in duty weapon.

Finally, the use of live weapons, particularly if they are individual duty weapons, for interleaved training involving live role-players does have the potential to increase the emotional content of the training sessions, thereby improving effectiveness. It may also help develop the practice of habitual equipment checks for things such as weapon condition and ammunition load of all magazines as a standard procedure when preparing for duty.

As every reader of this book already knows, the use of live weapons in this manner also has potential drawbacks. The first and most obvious is the fact that live weapons can fire live rounds, which means that the potential for serious injury or death during such training evolutions can never be completely eliminated. The second drawback, particularly if individual duty weapons are used, is that several extra minutes are required in the overall training time on each end to ensure that individuals have the opportunity and environment to properly unload their weapons safely. Formal safety checks must also be conducted before training commences. Following training, the reverse must occur, as officers must place their weapons back into the desired duty condition. Finally, wear and tear may become an issue when using live weapons, as some are not designed with dry-fire in mind. There is at least one handgun model in relatively common use by law enforcement agencies that we are aware of that will suffer a catastrophic breakage of the firing pin if dry fired extensively. Therefore, it is important to check with the weapon manufacturer to ensure that weapons and other related equipment that may be counted upon operationally are not broken through the training method.[24]

---

[24] Some risk of using live weapons may be mitigated through the use of dummy magazines or modified magazines (for example removing the followers) if using magazine-fed weapons. Note that this does not preclude the potential for chambering and firing a live round and that some functional weapon features (such as the slide locking back automatically on an empty chamber) may not function properly if this is done.

Barrel Inserts/Replacements

A number of manufacturers have designed tools to mitigate the potential for serious injury or death during dry-fire training. These include barrel flags, chamber inserts, and barrel replacements, which preclude the possibility of a live round being chambered and/or fired and also provide an externally visible signature, showing that they are in place. We have not evaluated any of these specific training tools, but believe that they have great potential value.

There are a few disadvantages and challenges associated with use of these types of risk-mitigating tools. The first is financial cost. While likely minimal, there is some cost associated with procurement. The second is dependence. If these tools become broken, lost, or simply left in the wrong place, their absence may preclude training from occurring. Use of these types of tools may also preclude the use of dummy rounds during training, which may make the conduct of some specific types of drills or exercises more difficult to set up. Finally, these individual tools will likely be caliber specific or perhaps even weapon specific. If individual officers have a choice in the weapons they carry, ensuring that the right training tools are on hand is more of a logistical challenge.

Simunition/UTM

One of the greatest advancements in training technology of the past two decades was the development of kits/tools that are designed to take functional duty weapons and turn them into the equivalent of paintball guns while maintaining both form and function. These tools are excellent for many training applications but are most often used for force-on-force training. But, since these weapon inserts are designed to prevent the chambering of a live round and normally permit the full functioning and mechanical operation of a weapon, they also can be used to mitigate the injury or death risk associated with dry-fire training methods.

The primary disadvantage of this method of risk reduction is cost, as these tools can be prohibitively expensive, particularly in the large numbers required to facilitate the desired repetitions associated with dry-fire training methodology. These kits may also preclude the use of dummy rounds and may be difficult to procure if a large number of individually chosen weapon systems are in use. Finally, it should be noted that while these kits may in some ways *reduce* the risk, they do not eliminate it. Manufacturers do not guarantee that their kit will fully prevent a live round from being fired, and the kits are designed to fire specialized, high-speed projectiles that can cause serious injury or even death if the proper protective equipment is not used.

Airsoft

Over the past decade, airsoft has become commonly used as sort of a "poor man's" force-on-force tool. Airsoft guns usually function similarly to live weapons but often contain some significant differences in fundamental function, and there are often great differences in feel, particularly with control and trigger manipulation. They are usually not as robust and can be prone to breaking if used for aggressive weapons-handling training, although this may depend on quality and specific manufacturer. Airsoft weapons may also be difficult to procure as substitutes for some weapons. Additionally, while usually less expensive than the Simunition or UTM alternatives, airsoft guns do still cost money. In our opinion, airsoft is an acceptable alternative for limited-scale force-on-force training; however, it is less then optimal as a dry-fire substitute.

Blanks/BFAs

The military has long used blanks as force-on-force training tools (sometimes combined with a laser system for use as a targeting and engagement-assessment tool). For this purpose, the tools utilized include fully functional weapons, magazines with blank ammunition, and a device called a blank-firing adaptor (BFA) that attaches to the end of a rifle muzzle. In our experience, these tools are commonly used only with service rifles. It is very important to note that *the use of a BFA does not preclude the chambering or firing of live ammunition.* For this and other reasons, in our opinion, the use of BFAs is not an acceptable risk-mitigation factor for dry-fire training.

SIRT Weapons

One of the most exciting and novel training tools to be developed within the past several years is the Shot Indicating Resetting Trigger (SIRT) tool available from Next Level Training. These laser-based systems are designed to allow for the practice of weapon presentation, trigger manipulation, trigger reset, and speed reloading. There is no potential for firing a projectile.

The current drawbacks to SIRT systems include their high cost (they may cost an organization as much or more than live weapons), the limited available configurations in terms of weapon systems, the inability to conduct drills that involve slide manipulation, and a base weapon setup that includes an extended magazine release, which may be different from that on a duty weapon. SIRT weapons also produce a laser when the trigger is pressed, designed for providing feedback to the shooter. This presents an eye-safety hazard to role-players. It also has the potential to train improper ocular focus to procedural memory if used improperly during training.

Armorer-Made Inert Weapons (Red Handles)

Finally, it is also possible to have live weapons made inert through the removal of firing pins or other modifications that preclude the firing of live ammunition yet leave the basic function and operation of the weapons themselves intact. These weapons are then usually marked in such a way as to identify them as inert (for example, the FBI once used red painted handles for this purpose). This technique may be cost prohibitive or cost-effective, depending on the size and resources of the organization as well as the locations and frequency of training.

Notes on Training Safety Structure

Given the potential for serious injury or death associated with any firearms training evolution, we feel that it is both responsible and appropriate within the context of the discussion above to share some considerations and procedural safety recommendations. We have found these to be effective at helping to mitigate training risks, particularly those associated with dry-fire and simulator training. (We do not intend for this section to be considered an all-inclusive or comprehensive guide to training safety. Such a guide is outside the scope and purpose of this book.)

1. Define a sterile area.

The critical component to safe dry-fire training is to ensure that no live ammunition is present in the training area. It is important to recognize that this should be adhered to *even if live weapons are not used* and may include the prohibition of live weapons as well as edged, energy, chemical, and impact weapons, depending upon the scope of the training and the equipment normally carried by the trainees. If a specific sterile area is well defined, it is both easier for trainees to comply with safety procedures and easier for instructors to enforce them.

2. Provide and define an administrative area to move from operational to sterile.

A great percentage of firearms accidents occur when users are changing the weapons from one condition to another. Live ammunition will always be present at this time and the condition of the weapon is changing, perhaps amid distraction. Overall, organizational training safety will be greatly enhanced by defining and providing a well-thought-out, stress-free, and well-structured area for this operation. The area should facilitate change (loading/ unloading, etc.) and include the storage of live ammunition and/or weapons. It should also have clearing barrels, or an equivalent, bulletproof option where loaded muzzles can be safety pointed.

3. Define a surface danger zone (SDZ) for the training area.

Dry-fire training, whether with live weapons or another option, *should not* involve the firing of live rounds. However, it is impossible to completely eliminate the risk regardless of which option is used. Therefore, it is worthwhile to consider the potential impact area associated with the primary direction of fire, even for dry-fire exercises.

4. Utilize procedure-based and redundant safety checks.

There are two certainties in life beyond death and taxes. Equipment will break and people will make mistakes. These truths cannot be ignored when developing training infrastructure, particularly for firearms training. Therefore, we have found it helpful and effective to implement formal and redundant safety protocols when conducting dry-fire and force-on-force training. There are varying structures, but the general concept is to notify each individual of the specific safety procedures and limitations required (for example, no live ammunition in the sterile area). Then each person is responsible for conducting a self-check for these prohibited items, to include weapons, pockets, magazines, pouches, and bags. Following this "self-check," a "buddy check" is conducted, where a second trainee conducts a hands-on inspection of the other person's equipment. Finally, an instructor (and/or role-player if used) will conduct at least a third complete hands-on inspection to ensure that the possibility for mishap has been mitigated acceptably.

5. Formalize and document accountability for safety-check procedures.

We have found it helpful to require formal documentation of these individual safety checks. This can be accomplished by requiring the name and signature (or initials) of each individual along with the name and initials of the person who conducts his or her specific "buddy check." Finally, the instructor (and/or role-player) must sign that he or she has inspected all individuals involved. In this way, there is a measure of individual accountability assigned to each individual for his or her own role within the safety protocols. This tends to enhance both the seriousness and quality of the safety inspections.

6. Run blocked skill-enhancement drills utilizing all kit before using role-players.

Even after these triple safety protocols are observed, we find it prudent to begin with a series of "warm up" skill-enhancement drills that require each individual student to work fully through his or her equipment with regards to weapons and magazines. This should occur regardless of how advanced the level of the training is and whether or not role-players will be used. This way, the opportunity for any stray live round or loaded magazine to be inserted into a weapon is provided *before* there is a possibility of a role-player facing the business end of a weapon. Note that this is highly recommended regardless of whether or not live weapons are used in the training. People make mistakes, and equipment breaks.

7. Consider the contextual and specific stimulus associations with role-players and dress.

While specific training techniques are outside the scope of this book, we have discussed the potential use of live role-players to facilitate incorporating stimulus recognition and decision-making components into interleaved training in a dry-fire environment. With this in mind, it is important to consider a couple of principles.

a. *This technique is not appropriate for all training environments and resource levels.* More specifically, individual members of a unit who work together in the field *should not* act as role-players for this type of training. Doing so raises the potential for removing the mental barriers to instigating a "blue on blue" engagement through development of a training scar.

b. Specific to law enforcement and military environments, law enforcement uniforms, badges, friendly military uniforms, and so on should never be worn by role-players who are intended to be engaged during the decision-making training.

173

Chapter 13

Areas and Opportunities for Future Research

We believe that this research, based on a combination of our own training and operational experiences with a literature review of applicable developmental psychology and neuroscience studies, has opened up some exciting possibilities for future projects that will build upon and enhance this body of work. Several of these are briefly discussed below.

We must collect empirical data comparing/contrasting operational results of the standard paradigm with operational results of applying our proposed training methodology.

We have used our basic training methodology extensively for several decades in a variety of environments. Therefore, we know from firsthand experience of its effectiveness. A growing number of trainers are beginning to take note of the same principles and are starting to conduct training in a similar fashion. Nonetheless, there has not been a peer-reviewed, scientifically rigorous study conducted to date that compares these training methods specifically with the commonly accepted training paradigm.

We feel that such research is both overdue and necessary to advance our industry. We look forward to either conducting this study ourselves or participating in it in the near future.

Do current training methods create stress-related brain injuries in training?

One of the most intriguing things that we discovered in our research of the procedural memory system is its seemingly symbiotic connection with emotion. Not only can emotion affect the formation of procedural memory, but it also appears that existing procedural memory can also affect emotion and emotional response to stimuli (Blanchard et al. 2001).

Over the past decade, one of the major developments in training for both military and law enforcement has been the more prevalent use of hyperrealistic force-on-force training designed to simulate actual combat/operational conditions. One of the objectives normally associated with hyperrealistic training scenarios is that of training the stress response to extinction based on the stimuli presented. In other words, the objective is to lessen the effects of the stress response once the student confronts actual combat by making the combat environment "normal" before it is actually encountered. When done successfully, combat becomes then not a "critical incident" by definition but rather an event within the normal realm of human experience.

Hyperrealistic training has proven to be very effective at accomplishing this goal and improving combat performance. However, we wonder if it may also be a contributing factor in what seems to be a greater prevalence of debilitating postcombat emotional trauma today than existed during previous conflicts, particularly in military personnel.

Due to the use of suboptimal training methodology as discussed in this book, very few personnel outside of specialized units ever actually develop the full body of procedurally consolidated motor skills or the full network of connected neural-networks to apply required skills operationally while they are involved in the training process. Nevertheless, they are repeatedly placed into hyperrealistic environments designed to produce the stress response to combat-related stimuli.

In less technical jargon and more to the point, most trainees are presented with problems that they do not have the capability to solve while the stress response is intentionally induced by the training environment. Most properly designed force-on-force training does not provide the students with the ability to "fail;" however, it is a certainty that most people know whether or not they would have succeeded had the bullets been real, regardless of the artificial training structure and instructor-designed outcomes.

In light of our research, which suggests the potential for instantaneously creating permanent neurological pathways when the stress hormones are present at high levels, we believe that this is an area where research should be conducted. We believe it is possible that hyperrealistic training, when given to students who do not have the procedurally consolidated skill set to solve the problem presented, may be responsible for causing (or at least contributing to) what are, in effect, permanent neurological injuries.

Can neurologically based methods of training system design reduce stress-related brain injuries in training?

In the context of the previous section, we wonder if our model for training system design might provide an alternative that could reduce the prevalence of stress-related injuries while achieving the same operational results. Training could be redesigned to construct fully consolidated skill sets into procedural memory (including the extensive use of interleaved training methodology) *before* students are intentionally exposed to stressful stimuli.

The objectives of improving operational performance and enhancing survivability through limiting the effects of the stress response during early exposure to combat would remain. However, the methodology employed would differ. Rather than taking the primary approach of training the stress response itself to extinction through repeated exposure, the concept would instead be to limit the occurrence and severity of the stress response by specifically coding the full scope of the skill set and stimulus responses required for operational performance into procedural memory. In essence then, the stimuli that are currently used to produce the stress response during hyperrealistic training are instead used to trigger access to procedurally consolidated neural-networks that correspond to operational performance.

Our own personal operational experiences provide support for this concept. Additionally, we have conducted anecdotal discussions with numerous highly trained and operationally experienced personnel. They report experiencing greater stress during training than during some combat operations as well as experiencing something akin to a euphoric calm rather than the expected effects of the sympathetic nervous system when engaged in actual combat.

While by no means conclusive, these experiences do suggest that improved procedural consolidation may in fact reduce the severity of the stress response during combat operations, perhaps with equal or greater effectiveness than training the stress response to extinction. Therefore, it is possible that improving procedural consolidation in training may potentially reduce the prevalence of stress-related brain injuries that occur in armed professionals.

Conclusion

The objective of this book has been to outline the principles behind our unique approach to tactical training system design and delivery as well as to document the neuroscience-based research that supports it.

The methods that produce the most effective results during the initial acquisition process into short-term memory are not necessarily the methods that produce the most effective operational results. This is an important concept for instructors and curriculum developers to understand, particularly given the undefined temporal nature of the operational requirements associated with applying tactical skills. In fact, the opposite may in many instances be true. Therefore, we propose that the firearms and tactical training industry should pause to consider the underlying structure and intent of its training methods and systems.

Teaching specific techniques and tactics is fine. Ultimately, however, we believe that there is usually more than one way to "skin a cat," as the saying goes. There are certainly some techniques or tactics that are in fact "wrong." But often the use of one over another can be distilled down to a discussion regarding the advantages and disadvantages of one versus the equally real advantages and disadvantages of the other, where both sides of the argument have a valid point. Furthermore, in many (if not most) cases, competent practitioners of either technique or tactic will be more than capable of superb operational performance.

We both encourage and appreciate (and may occasionally participate in) passionate discussions, arguments, and disagreements about specific techniques and tactics. However, in light of our experience and research, we also believe that conducting a fundamental reevaluation of the basic methodology that our industry utilizes in attempting to produce competent practitioners of the skills and concepts we teach is ultimately an area with more potential for significant change. We believe that making a fundamental change in how we train provides the greatest opportunity to make a positive impact on the industry at large, affecting both training and operations.

Thank you for providing us the opportunity to share some of our research and experience. We hope that it has provided, at the very least, the opportunity for a new viewpoint on both how and why firearms and tactical training should be designed and delivered. Please join us in working to advance our industry by improving both the quality and effectiveness of training. And to all those who are still in harm's way and live their lives "on the X"…thank you.

—The Innovative Services and Solutions Team

Appendix A:
Instructor-Controllable Factors
That Influence Procedural Consolidation

- Priming
  - This should occur twenty-four to forty-eight hours prior to instruction.

- Repetition
  - This is the single most important factor in connectionist learning.

- Observation
  - This should happen after practice occurs (within the session).
  - It should be seven minutes in length.
  - It requires intent to replicate.
  - It should be side/limb specific.
  - Avoid expertise reversal by not utilizing it after skilled performance is achieved.
  - It can be applied to cognitive tasks, decision-making, and problem solving but only with advanced students who already possess the full body of skills within the procedural memory.

- Emotional Connection (chemical change resulting from stimuli or process)
  - Procedural memories will affect future emotional responses.
  - Fear inhibits most learning.

- o Fear instantly creates powerful associations that may be unwanted.
- o Emotional connection to stimuli or context improves learning retention.
- o Emotional arousal after the training period enhances emotional connection effects.

- Stress
  - o Low-level stress improves learning performance in males only.
  - o Positive effects of low-level stress are enhanced by emotional connection.
  - o High-level stress acts like fear, creating powerful connections yet inhibiting most learning processes.

- Off-Line Time (waking)
  - o Waking off-line time consolidates physical skills.
  - o Consolidation effects are limited to learning.
  - o Consolidation process inhibits recall and performance.

- Off-Line Time (sleep)
  - o Sleep consolidates the goals and visuomotor elements of skill performance.
  - o Consolidation effects are limited to learning.
  - o Sleep develops novel connections between data points.
  - o Sleep enhances problem solving and decision-making abilities.
  - o Sleep period must occur within twelve hours of learning in order to be effective.

- Exercise
    - Exercise improves learning transfer and associative learning.

- Interleaved Training
    - It is chaotic training.
    - It reduces end-of-training performance standards.
    - It improves long-term retention.
    - It improves operational performance.
    - When used alone, it will act as a governor with highly technical skills.

- Interference
    - A twenty-four-hour learning gap is required to eliminate interference.
    - Multiple responses to a single stimulus will result in interference effects during performance.
    - Contextual association can reduce interference effects.

- Declarative Learning
    - Declarative and procedural consolidation processes interfere with each other.
    - Pick one kind of learning or the other as an objective but not both.
    - It is the processes that interfere, not the information storage.

- Time of Day
    - Teaching that occurs in the late afternoon has been shown to result in improved retention and long-term learning performance.

Appendix B:
Summary of Recommendations to Apply
Research to Tactical Training System Design

1.   Tactical training systems design should be restructured from outcome-based performance evaluation to targeted neural-network development and enhancement.

2.   Standards are tools for liability control, administrative control, and training system feedback; they should neither be viewed nor utilized as a training objective.

3.   Training systems should be fundamentally restructured based on how the human brain learns and retains skills and information.

     a.   Training systems should be designed so that the students effectively learn all of the information as it is presented.

     b.   Specific periods of instruction should be designed to only present the amount of information that can be coded into the short-term memory system.

     c.   Following training periods, both waking and sleep off-line time should be provided to the students within twelve hours.

d.   There should be at least twenty-four hours separating instructional periods that will cover new skills and/or information that utilize the same neural space within short-term memory.

e.   Periods of instruction should make intentional, informed use of the instructor-controllable factors that influence procedural consolidation.

4.   After skills and information have been consolidated to long-term memory, the majority of the available training time should be focused on applying interleaved training methodology.

References

Aeschbach, D., A. J. Cutler, and J. M. Ronda. "A Role for Non-Rapid-Eye-Movement Sleep Homeostasis in Perceptual Learning." *The Journal of Neuroscience* 28, no. 11 (2008): 2766–72.

Agnew, Z. K., S. Brownsett, Z. Woodhead, and X. de Boissezon. "A Step Forward for Mirror Neurons? Investigating the Functional Link between Action Execution and Action Observation in Limb Apraxia." *The Journal of Neuroscience* 28, no. 31 (2008): 7726–27.

Albert, N. B., E. M. Robertson, P. Mehta, R. C. Miall. "Resting State Networks and Memory Consolidation." *Communicative and Integrative Biology* 2, no. 6 (2009): 530–32.

Albert, N. B., E. M. Robertson, and R. C. Miall. "The Resting Human Brain and Motor Learning." *Current Biology* 19 (2009): 1023–27.

Ans, B., S. Rousset, R. M. French, and S. Musca. "Preventing Catastrophic Interference in Multiple-Sequence Learning Using Coupled Reverberating Elman Networks." In *Proceedings of the 24th Annual Conference of the Cognitive Science Society*, 2002.

Bates, M. "The Mind Is a Mirror." 2009. http://www.scientificamerican.com/article.cfm?id=the-mind-is-a-mirror.

Becker, S., G. MacQueen, and J. M. Wojtowicz. "Computational Modeling and Empirical Studies of Hippocampal Neurogenesis-Dependent Memory: Effects of Interference, Stress and Depression." http://www.science.mcmaster.ca/Psychology/sb.html.

Blanchard, C., R. Blanchard, J. M. Fellous, F. S. Guimaraes, W. Irwin, J. E. LeDoux, J. L. McGaugh, J. B. Rosen, L. C. Schenberg, E. Volchan, and C. Da Cunha. "The Brain Decade in Debate: III. Neurobiology of Emotion." *Brazilian Journal of Medical and Biological Research* 34 (2001): 283–93.

Berthouze, L. and A. Tijsseling. "A Neural Model for Context-Dependent Sequence Learning." *Neural Processing Letters* 23 (2006): 27–45.

Biedka, T., B. Dreger, J. Kachlicki, K. Krawiek, M. Plazewski, P. Wierzejewski, and P. Wozniak. "Employing a Neural Network to Solving the Repetition Spacing Problem," 1998. http://www.supermemo.com/english/ol/nn.htm.

Brashers-Krug, T., R. Shadmehr, and E. Torodov. "Catastrophic Interference in Human Motor Learning." *Advances in Neural Information Processing Systems* 3, no.7 (1995).

Brawn, T. P., K. M. Fenn, H. C. Nusbaum, and D. Margoliash. "Consolidating the Effects of Waking and Sleep on Motor Sequence Learning." *The Journal of Neuroscience* 30, no. 42 (2010): 13977–82.

Brown, R. M. and E. M. Robertson. "Off-Line Processing: Reciprocal Interactions between Declarative and Procedural Memories." *The Journal of Neuroscience* 27, no. 39 (2007): 10468–75.

Buccino, G. and L. Riggio. "The Role of the Mirror Neuron System in Motor Learning." *Kinesiology* 38 (2006).

Caithness, G., R. Osu, P. Bays, H. Chase, J. Klassen, M. Kawato, D. M. Wolpert, and J. R. Flanagan. "Failure to Consolidate: The Consolidation Theory of Learning for Sensorimotor Adaptation Tasks." *The Journal of Neuroscience* 24, no. 40 (2004): 8662–71.

Catmur, C., H. Gillmeister, G. Bird, R. Liepelt, M. Brass, and C. Heyes. "Through the Looking Glass: Counter-Mirror Activation Following Incompatible Sensorimotor Learning." *European Journal of Neuroscience* 28 (2008): 1208–15.

Chang, Q. and P. E. Gold. "Switching Memory Systems During Learning: Changes in the Patterns of Brain Acetylcholine Release in the Hippocampus and Striatum in Rats." *The Journal of Neuroscience* 23, no. 7 (2008): 3001–5.

Cohen, D. A., A. Pascual-Leone, D. Z. Press, and E. M. Robertson. "Off-Line Learning of Motor Skill Memory: A Double Dissociation of Goal and Movement." In *Proceedings of the National Academy of Sciences of the United States of America* 102, no. 50 (2005): 18237–41. doi: 10.1073/pnas.0506072102.

Colon-Cesario, M., J. Wang, X. Ramos, H. G. Garcia, J. J. Davila, J. Laguna, C. Rosado, and S. Pena de Ortiz. "An Inhibitor of DNA Recombination Blocks Memory Consolidation, but Not Reconsolidation, in Context Fear Conditioning." *The Journal of Neuroscience* 26, no. 20 (2006): 5524–33.

Cooke, S. F., P. J. E. Attwell, and C. H. Yeo. "Temporal Properties of Cerebral-Dependent Memory Consolidation." *The Journal of Neuroscience* 24, no. 12 (2004): 2934–41.

Criscimagna-Hemminger, S. E. and R. Shadmehr. "Consolidation Patterns of Human Motor Memory." *The Journal of Neuroscience* 28, no. 39 (2008): 9610–18.

Cross, E. S., P.J. Schmitt, and S. T. Grafton. "Neural Substrates of Contextual Interference During Motor Learning Support a Model of Active Preparation." *Journal of Cognitive Neuroscience* 19, no. 11 (2007): 1854–71.

Cuttrel, E., M. Czerwinski, and E. Horvitz. "Notification, Disruption, and Memory: Effects of Messaging Interruptions on Memory and Performance." *Human-Computer Interaction—Interact '01* (2001): 263–69.

Della-Maggiore, V. "Motor Memory Consolidation, Night and Day." *The Journal of Neuroscience* 25, no. 40 (2005): 9067–68.

Denning, J. "Tactical Training Tips: Key Points for Instructors and Shooters." *Action Target Journal* (2011).Retrieved December 1, 2011. http://www.actiontarget.com/tactical-training-tips-key-points-for-instructors-shooters/.

Dennis, S. and J. Wiles. "Integrating Learning into Models of Human Memory: Hebbian Recurrent Network." 1993.

Dreger, B. and P. Wozniak. "Implementing the Repetition Spacing Neural Network." 1998. http://www.supermemo.com/english/ol/nn_train.htm.

Duncko, R., B. Cornwell, L. Cui, K. R. Merikangas, and C. Grillon. "Acute Exposure to Stress Improves Performance in Trace Eyeblink Conditioning and Spatial Learning Tasks in Healthy Men." *Learning & Memory* 14, no. 5 (2007): 329–35.

Duncko, R., L. Johnson, K. Merlkangas, and C. Grillon. "Working Memory Performance after Acute Exposure to the Cold Pressor Stress in Healthy Volunteers." *Neurobiology of Learning and Memory* 91, no. 4 (2009): 377–81.

Ericsson, K. A., R. T. Krampe, and C. Tesch-Romer. "The Role of Deliberate Practice in the Acquisition of Expert Performance." *Psychological Review* 100, no. 3 (1993): 363–406.

Fischer, S., M. F. Nitschke, U. H. Melchert, C. Erdmann, and J. Born. "Motor Memory Consolidation in Sleep Shapes More Effective Neuronal Representations." *The Journal of Neuroscience* 25, no. 49 (2005): 1248–55.

French, R. M. and A. Ferrara. "Modeling Time Perception in Rats: Evidence for Catastrophic Interference in Animal Learning." In *Proceedings of the 21st Annual Conference of the Cognitive Science Conference,*173–78. 1999.

Frey, S. H. and V. E. Gerry. "Modulation of Neural Activity During Observational Learning of Actions and Their Sequential Orders." *The Journal of Neuroscience* 26, no. 51 (2006): 13194–201.

Grafton, S. T., E. Hazeltine, and R. Ivry. "Functional Mapping of Sequence Learning in Normal Humans." *Journal of Cognitive Neuroscience* 7, no. 4 (1995): 497–510.

Grossman, D. and B. K. Siddle. "Psychological Effects of Combat." *Academic Press* (2000). http://www.killology.com/print/print_psychological.htm.

Hattori, M. "Avoiding Catastrophic Forgetting by a Dual-Network Memory Model Using a Chaotic Neural Network." *World Academy of Science, Engineering and Technology* 60 (2009): 851–55.

Jensen, E. *Brain-Based Learning: The New Paradigm of Teaching.*California:Corwin Press, 2008.

Jin, Y. and B. Sendhoff. "Alleviating Catastrophic Forgetting via Multi-Objective Learning." In *2006 International Joint Conference on Neural Networks*, 6367–74.2006.

Joels, M., Z. Pu, O. Wiegert, M. S. Oitzl, and J. H. Krugers. "Learning Under Stress: How Does It Work?" *Trends in Cognitive Sciences* 10 (2006): 152–58.

Kassardjian, C. D., Y. Tan, J. J. Chung, R. Heskin, M. J. Peterson, and D. M. Broussard. "The Site of a Motor Memory Shifts with Consolidation." *The Journal of Neuroscience* 25, no. 35 (2005): 7979–85.

Kilner, J. M., A. Neal, N. Weiskopf, K. J. Friston, and C. D. Frith. "Evidence of Mirror Neurons in Human Inferior Frontal Gyrus." *The Journal of Neuroscience* 29, no. 32 (2009): 10153–59.

Kim, J. J., H. J. Lee, J. Han, and M. G. Packard. "Amygdala is Critical for Stress-Induced Modulation of Hippocampal Long-Term Potentiation and Learning." *The Journal of Neuroscience* 21, no. 14 (2001): 5222–28.

Kleim, J. A., T. M. Hogg, P. M. VandenBerg, N. R. Cooper, R. Bruneau, and M. Remple. "Cortical Synaptogenesis and Motor Map Reorganization Occur During Late, but Not Early, Phase of Motor Skill Learning." *The Journal of Neuroscience* 24, no. 3 (2004): 628–33.

Krakauer, J. W., C. Ghez, and F. M. Ghilardi. "Adaptation to Visuomotor Transformations: Consolidation, Interference, and Forgetting." *The Journal of Neuroscience* 25, no. 2 (2005): 473–8.

Kratzig, G. P. "Pistol Skill Acquisition and Retention: A Three-Year Longitudinal Study." In *Interservice/Industry Training, Simulation, and Education Conference*, 2014.

Kratzig, G. P. and C. Hudy. "From Theory to Practice: Simulation Technology as a Training Tool in Law Enforcement." In *Police Organization and Training: Innovations in Research and Practice*, edited by M. R. Haberfield, Curtis A. Clark, and Dale L. Heehan. New York: Springer, 2011.

Kratzig, G. P., M. Hyde, and C. Parker. "Pistol Skills Transfer from a Synthetic Environment to Real World Setting." In *Interservice/Industry Training, Simulation, and Education Conference*, 2011.

Krugers, H. J., M. Zhou, M. Joels, and M. Kindt. "Regulation of Excitatory Synapses and Fearful Memories by Stress Hormones." *Frontiers in Behavioral Neuroscience* 5, no. 62 (2011).

189

Kuriyama, K., K. Mishima, H. Suzuki, S. Aritake, and M. Uchiyama. "Sleep Accelerates the Improvement in Working Memory Performance." *The Journal of Neuroscience* 28, no. 40 (2008): 10145–50.

Lee, H. J., Y. W. Park, D. H. Jeong, and H. Y. Jung. "Effects of Night Sleep on Motor Learning Using Transcranial Magnetic Stimulation." *Annals of Rehabilitation Medicine* 36 (2012): 226–32.

Lenne, M. G."A Review of Critical Human Factors Issues for Aviation Team Training." *Defence Science & Technology* (2003).

Lin C. H., B. J. Knowlton, M. C. Chiang, M. Iacoboni, P. Udompholkul, and A. D. Wu. "Brain-Behavior Correlates of Optimizing Learning through Interleaved Practice." *Neuroimage* 56, no. 3 (2011): 1758–72.

Lin, C., B. E. Fisher, C. J. Winstein, A. D. Wu, and J. Gordon. "Contextual Interference Effect: Elaborative Processing or Forgetting-Reconstruction? A Post Hoc Analysis of Transcranial Magnetic Stimulation-Induced Effects on Motor Learning." *Journal of Motor Behavior* 40, no. 6 (2008). http://www.tandfonline.com/doi/abs/10.3200/JMBR.40.6.578-586?url_ver=Z39.88-2003&rfr_id=ori:rid:crossref.org&rfr_dat=cr_pub%3dpubmed&.

Lin, C., B. E. Fisher, A. D. Wu, Y. Ko, L. Lee, and C. J. Winstein."Neural Correlate of the Contextual Interference Effect in Motor Learning: A Kinematic Analysis." *Journal of Motor Behavior* 41, no. 3 (2009):232–42.

Ma, L., S. Narayana, D. A. Rogin, P. T. Fox, and J. Xiong. "Changes Occur in Resting State Network of Motor System During 4 Weeks of Motor Skill Learning." *Neuroimage* 58, no. 1 (2011): 226–33. doi: 10.1016/j.neuroimage.2011.06.014.

Maquet, P., S. Schwartz, R. Passingham, and C. Frith. "Sleep-Related Consolidation of a Visuomotor Skill: Brain Mechanisms as Assessed by Functional Magnetic Resonance Imaging." *The Journal of Neuroscience* 23, no. 4 (2003): 1432–40.

Mareschal, D. and R. M. Franch. "A Connectionist Account of Interference Effects in Early Infant Memory and Categorization." In *Proceedings of the 19th Annual Cognitive Science Society Conference*, 484–9. 1997.

McClelland, J. L., B. L. McNaughton, and R. C. O'Reilly. "Why There Are Complementary Learning Systems in the Hippocampus and Neocortex: Insights from the Successes and Failures of Connectionist Models of Learning and Memory." *Psychological Review* 102, no. 3 (1995): 419–57.

McIntyre, C. K., and B. Roozendaal. "Adrenal stress hormones and enhanced memory for emotionally arousing experiences."In *Neural Plasticity and Memory: From Genes to Brain Imaging*, edited by Frederico Bermúdez-Rattoni. Boca Raton: CRC Press, 2007.

McRae, K. and P. A. Hetherington. "Catastrophic Interference Is Eliminated in Pretrained Networks." University of Rochester; McGill University.

Mirman, D. and M. Spivey. "Retroactive Interference in Neural Networks and in Humans: The Effect of Pattern-Based Learning." *Connection Science* 13, no. 3 (2001): 257–75.

Mohns, J. E. and M. S. Blumberg. "Synchronous Bursts of Neuronal Activity in the Developing Hippocampus: Modulation by Active Sleep and Association with Emerging Gamma and Theta Rhythms." *The Journal of Neuroscience* 28, no. 40 (2008): 10134–44.

Montgomery, S. M., A. Sirota, and G. Buzsaki. "Theta and Gamma Coordination of Hippocampal Networks During Waking and Rapid Eye Movement Sleep." *The Journal of Neuroscience* 28, no. 26 (2008): 6731–41.

Murre, J. "Transfer of Learning in Backpropagation and in Related Neural Network Models." In *Connectionist Models of Memory and Language*. London: UCL Press.

Pennartz, C. M. A., J. D. Berke, A. M. Graybiel, R. Ito, C. S. Lansink, M. van der Meer, A. D. Redish, K. S. Smith, and P. Voorn. "Corticostriatal Interactions During Learning, Memory Processing, and Decision Making." *The Journal of Neuroscience* 29, no. 41 (2009): 12831–8.

Rauchs, G., D. Feyers, B. Landeau, C. Bastin, A. Luxen, P. Maquet, and F. Collette. "Sleep Contributes to the Strengthening of Some Memories over Others, Depending on Hippocampal Activity at Learning." *The Journal of Neuroscience* 31, no. 7 (2011): 2563–8.

Rash, C. E., K. L. Hiatt, R. M. Widzunas, J. L. Caldwell, J. A. Caldwell, M. E. Kalich, G. T. Lang, R. P. King, and R. Noback. "Perceptual and Cognitive Effects Due to Operational Factors." http://www.usaarl.army.mil/publications/HMD_Book09/files/Section%2024%20-Chapter16%20Perceptual%20and%20Cognitive%20Effects%20Due%20to%20Operational%20Factors.pdf.

Richardson, A. G., S. A. Overduin, A. Valero-Cabre, C. Padoa-Schioppa, A. Pascual-Leone, E. Bizzi, and D. Z. Press. "Disruption of Primary Motor Cortex before Learning Impairs Memory of Movement Dynamics." *The Journal of Neuroscience* 26, no. 48 (2006): 12466–70.

Robertson, E. M. "From Creation to Consolidation: A Novel Framework for Memory Processing." *PLoS Biology* 7, no. 1 (2009). doi: 10.1371/journal.pbio.1000019.

Robertson, E. M., D. Z. Press, and A. Pascual-Leone. "Off-Line Learning and the Primary Motor Cortex." *The Journal of Neuroscience* 25, no. 27 (2005):6372–8.

Rosenthal, C. R., E. E. Roche-Kelly, M. Hussain, and C. Kennard. "Response-Dependent Contributions of Human Primary Motor Cortex and Angular Gyrus to Manual and Perceptual Sequence Learning." *The Journal of Neuroscience* 29, no. 48 (2009):15115–25.

Sakai, K., O. Hikosala, S. Miyauchi, R. Takino, Y. Sasaki, and B. Putz. "Transition of Brain Activation from Frontal to Parietal Areas in Visuomotor Sequence Learning." *The Journal of Neuroscience* 18, no. 5 (1998): 1827–40.

Santini, E., R. U. Muller, and G. J. Quirk. "Consolidation of Extinction Learning Involves Transfer from NMDA-Independent to NMDA-Dependent Memory." *The Journal of Neuroscience* 21, no. 22 (2001): 9009–17.

Sarle, W. S. 2000. ai-faq/neural-nets/part2. Retrieved September 1, 2012. http://www.cs.rochester.edu/u/sanders/ml/neural_network_faq/FAQ2.html

Schwabe, L., O. T. Wolf, and M. S. Oitzl. "Memory Formation under Stress: Quantity and Quality." *Neuroscience and Biobehavioral Reviews* 34 (2010): 584–91.

Shadmehr, R., T. Brashers-Krug, and F. Mussa-Ivaldi. "Interference of Learning Internal Models of Inverse Dynamics in Humans." *Advances in Neural Information Processing Systems* 7 (1995): 1117–24.

Shadmehr, R. and T. Brashers-Krug. "Functional Stages in the Formation of Human Long-Term Motor Memory." *TheJournal of Neuroscience* 17 (1997): 409–19.

Schacter, D. L. "Implicit Memory: History and Current Status." *Journal of Experimental Psychology* 13, no. 3 (1987): 501–18.

Schmuelof, L. and E. Zohary. "A Mirror Representation of Other's Actions in the Human Anterior Parietal Cortex." *The Journal of Neuroscience* 26, no. 38 (2006): 9736–42.

Shi, C. and M. Davis. "Visual Pathways Involved in Fear Conditioning Measured with Fear-Potentiated Startle: Behavioral and Anatomic Studies." *The Journal of Neuroscience* 21, no. 24 (2001): 9844–55.

Shumway-Cooke, A. and M. H. Woollacott. *Motor Control: Translating Research into Clinical Practice.*Baltimore: Lippincott, Williams, and Wilkins, 2012.

Song, S., J. H. Howard Jr., and D. V. Howard. "Sleep Does Not Benefit Probabilistic Motor Sequence Learning." *The Journal of Neuroscience* 27, no. 46 (2007): 12475–83.

Steele, C. J. and V. B. Penhune. "Specific Increases within Global Decreases: A Functional Magnetic Resonance Imaging Investigation of Five Days of Motor Sequence Learning." *The Journal of Neuroscience* 30, no. 24 (2010): 8332–41.

Stefan, K., L. G. Cohen, J. Duque, R. Mazzocchio, P. Celnik, L. Sawaki, L. Ungerleider, and J. Classen. "Formation of a Motor Memory by Action Observation." *The Journal of Neuroscience* 25, no. 41 (2005): 9339–46.

Steidl, S., S. Mohi-uddin, and A.K. Anderson. "Effects of Emotional Arousal on Multiple Memory Systems: Evidence from Declarative and Procedural Learning." *Learning & Memory* 13, no. 5 (2006): 650–8.

Thomas, L. A. and K. S. LaBar. "Fear Relevancy, Strategy Use, and Probabilistic Learning of Cue-Outcome Associations." *Learning & Memory* 15, no. 10 (2008): 777–84.

Tong, C., D. M. Wolpert, and J. R. Flanagan. "Kinematics and Dynamics Are Not Represented Independently in Motor Working Memory: Evidence from an Interference Study." *The Journal of Neuroscience* 22, no. 3 (2002): 1108–13.

US Air Force Academy. *In-Flight Decision Making by High Time and Low Time Pilots During Instrument Operations*, by K. L. Kemper. Urbana, Illinois: University of Illinois, 1992.

US Army Research Institute. *Soldier Performance in Continuous Operations*, by F. Kopstein, A. Siegel, J. Conn, J. Caviness, W. Slifer, H. Ozkaptan, and F. Dyer. Wayne, PA: Applied Psychological Services Inc., 1985.

US Department of Transportation. Federal Aviation Administration. *How Expert Pilots Think: Cognitive Processes in Expert Decision Making*, by R. J. Adams. Jupiter, FL: Advanced Aviation Concepts, Inc., 1993.

Van Gog, T., F. Paas, N. Marcus, P. Ayres, and J. Sweller. "The Mirror Neuron System and Observational Learning: Implications for the Effectiveness of Dynamic Visualizations." *Educational Psychology Review* 21 (2009): 21–30.

Vickers, J. N. *Perception, Cognition, and Decision Training: The Quiet Eye in Action.* Champain: Human Kinetics, 2007.

Wang, D. and B. Yuwono. "Incremental Learning of Complex Temporal Patterns." *IEEE Transactions on Neural Networks* 7, no. 6 (1996): 1465–81.

Wiskott, L., M. J. Rasch, and G. Kempermann. "What Is the Functional Role of Adult Neurogenesis in the Hippocampus?" *Cognitive Sciences* (2004). https://cogprints.org/4012.

Wolf, O. T. "HPA Axis and Memory."*Best Practice and Research Clinical Endocrinology and Metabolism* 17, no. 2 (2003):287–99.

Wolfe, P. *Brain Matters: Translating Research into Classroom Practice.* Alexandria: ASCD, 2010.

Wright-Patterson Air Force Base. 1992. *Automatic Information Processing and High Performance Skills*, by F. T. Eggemeier and A. D. Fisk. Dayton, OH: Armstrong Laboratory, Logistics Research Division.

Zhang, X., T. T. de Beukelaar, J. Possel, M. Olaerts, S. P. Swinnen, D. G. Wooley, and N. Wenderoth. "Movement Observation Improves Early Consolidation of Motor Memory." *The Journal of Neuroscience* 31, no. 32 (2011): 11515–20.

Made in the USA
Las Vegas, NV
20 December 2021

39008026R00109